THE GREAT MIGRATIONS

By GEORGES BLOND

The Plunderers
The Death of Hitler's Germany
The Great Migrations

THE
GREAT MIGRATIONS

by

GEORGES BLOND

Translated by Frances Frenaye

THE MACMILLAN COMPANY
New York — 1960

Second Printing 1960

PRINTED IN THE UNITED STATES OF AMERICA

This book was published in France under the title
LA GRANDE AVENTURE DES MIGRATEURS.

Library of Congress catalog card number: 56–11445

INTRODUCTION

Day and night, from one end of the year to the other, while
we work or sleep or dream, even at the very moment when
you read these lines, there ceaselessly recurs a mysterious
planetary phenomenon, of which we are for the most part
unaware. Millions of living creatures are moving through air
and land and sea, just as they have moved for hundreds of
thousands of years, weaving around the globe a network of
peregrinations, some of them six thousand miles long.

In the course of their journeys, migratory animals deploy
an amount of energy out of all proportion to their size and
apparent physical resources; they triumph over obstacles
which man, even with the aid of his machines, might find
insuperable. Without benefit of maps, compasses, or instruments of observation, they steer, in every sort of weather, a
course as direct as if some mysterious guide were going before them.

To give this guide the name of instinct is to beg the question. Instinct does not account for the fact that certain species
are irresistibly impelled to migrate, while others that live
beside them remain, in the naturalists' term, sedentary, attached to their portion of native land or water.

For a long time I was haunted by the thought of this irresistible impulse and the great, ceaseless movement which it
entails. I wished to see the mysterious phenomenon at closer

range and to share my widened view. For we examine most thoroughly that which we have undertaken to describe to others.

To set out to see the phenomenon with my own eyes would have been ridiculous presumption. And so, just as I had spelled out various episodes of the Second World War by assembling a large number of fragmentary accounts and then piecing them together, so now I followed in naturalists' notebooks the adventures of migratory animals. Few subjects, it happens, have been submitted to so much scrutiny and revision in recent years. As a result, many of the most interesting books are either incomplete or outdated. In order to avoid falling into error I turned to the results of the latest scientific research, and in my effort first to comprehend and then to interpret them I found that I had a very great deal to learn.

Having conscientiously instructed myself, I proceeded to treat the material not as a scientist but as a writer. In the following pages I have purposely held technical explanations to the strict minimum necessary for understanding. I have told the odyssey not of every migratory species but only of a few among them, the most typical and to some extent the most dramatic. My choice is not based merely upon the reader's delectation; the combination of episodes should be such as to convince him of the reality of the phenomenon as it is known today.

My particular gratitude is due to Professor Budker, assistant director of the Muséum National d'Histoire Naturelle, who upon my ignorant approach to this whole subject started me off in the right direction. Whatever welcome my book may find, I shall not regret the effort put into my study. For after it was completed the great migrations seemed to me more fascinating than ever.

CONTENTS

	Introduction	v
I	*An Odyssey of Birds*	1
II	*Navigators Without a Compass*	49
III	*The Buffalo Trails*	102
IV	*The Eighth Plague*	135
V	*The Race to Destruction*	165

CHAPTER I

AN ODYSSEY OF BIRDS

1

The man was bracing himself against a wall of rock which rose vertically more than six hundred feet above him. His crushing load, whose weight was at least as great as his own, was jammed against the wall. He could just manage to maintain this position by the wide spread of his spindly legs, which were already trembling in a pair of blue cotton trousers, and indeed were visibly on the point of giving way. He wore tattered, rope-soled, canvas shoes, which had held out only by a miracle this far, and his torn trousers flapped like a flag in the freezing wind that blew over the whole width of the mountain pass. It was only August, and the wind came from the south, but for all that it was icy. The caravan, with its bearers and horses, was making its way slowly and painfully over the mountains, battling against the wind, and the man leaning his back against the wall of rock surveyed it with an impenetrable expression.

He might have been thirty-five years old, or else sixty—how is one to guess at the age of a Chinaman? This human machine, worn down to the thread, had no age whatsoever. His skinny forearms emerged from the amputated sleeves of an American army jacket, which had incredibly bargained and bartered its way to the heart of Asia, The caravan was traveling from Qulja to Aqsu, on the edge of the desert, three hundred miles as the crow flies, and the horses seemed as near the point of collapse as the men. From Qulja to the Muzart Pass, they had covered two hundred miles, most of it through the mountains.

The man leaning against the rock, whose knees were now slightly bent, so that he was even less erect than before, had covered the two hundred miles in the following manner: first he took fifty short, quick steps, with his back bent under his load at a 45-degree angle; then he stopped, stuck his stick into the ground or ice, spread his two hands over the top and let his stomach rest upon them, while he breathed heavily, making a noise like that of a pair of defective bellows. Two to five seconds later, he began the cycle again with fifty more steps. For at least two hundred years, as every traveler's account tells us, the technique has been exactly the same, and caravan bearers have carried as much as two hundred and fifty pounds of tea on their backs. Naturally, they do not live to a ripe old age; but then, in most of Asia, the care and feeding of a man is less expensive than that of a horse.

The Muzart Pass is in the middle of the high central range of the Tien Shan Mountains: a vast agglomeration in Turkestan, whose area is greater than that of France. These mountains are never in the newspapers; they hold no interest for famous climbers, because their highest peak is only about twenty-four thousand feet above sea level. Indeed, the topography of the central range is in many places uncertainly defined, for few geographers are tempted to haul their instruments to this far-away and chaotic region. And any pilot who flies over it watches his dials and listens to his motors with particular attention, knowing that a landing is impossible and a parachute jump would unquestionably be the pre-

lude to slow death from exposure. The Muzart Pass crosses
this range at an altitude of twelve thousand feet, rimmed by
glaciers which sweep down from the surrounding mountains,
every one of them higher than the Mont Blanc. For three-
quarters of the year, violent winds raise tempests of snow.
The whole length of the pass and some distance to either
side are littered with bones, but snow conceals them most of
the time from view.

The man leaning against the rock watched as the caravan
passed slowly before him. Every now and then a bearer, with
his back bent at a 45-degree angle, stopped to rest on his
stick. The furious blast of the wind and the chatter of a
mountain stream smothered the bearers' groaning sighs and
the tread of the horses, which other men, bending their
bodies to meet the wind's impact, were leading by their
bridles. The men moved like so many pale ghosts, and indeed
their whole existence had something unreal and ghostlike
about it.

For convenience, let us give the man leaning against the
rock a name. Let us call him Chuan. It is more than likely
that neither this name nor any other which the reader may
choose was ever entered in the birth records of a village or
town. A peasant family from the borderland of Chinese Turkestan has little legal existence, and for years no one had had
occasion to call Chuan anything at all. A caravan bearer
doesn't wait to be called; he is there, with fifty ghostly companions, and if he is not there no one is going to miss him. He
may be dead, or he may be curled up in a corner, smoking
remnants of opium; it doesn't really matter.

Chuan felt himself slipping, and closed his eyes. His legs
had crumpled, and finally he sat on his haunches, with his
load resting partially on the ground although the straps still

dug into his shoulders. From this sloping position he could
no longer see the stooping men of the caravan pass before
him. His head was turned slightly to the right, and beyond
the pass, to the southeast, between two snow-clad mountains,
he saw a slope, slightly lower than the rest, covered with
pines. The dark green trees, with a ray of sunlight upon them,
stood in closed ranks, like the soldiers of a motionless army.
Neither poverty nor wind had bent them over; they carried
no load and stood marvelously straight, just as they had
grown, pointing toward the sky. The picture they made was
one of dignity and freedom and power.

Chuan relaxed his legs and stretched them out in front of
him. Still feeling the straps cut into the area between his
chest and his shoulders, he threw back the upper part of his
body and at once obtained relief. The pine forest was now
lower in his line of vision, and without moving his head he
could see a large part of the snowy mountain summits.
Twenty times or more he had crossed the Tien Shan Mountains, and his eyes had been blinded by the dazzling whiteness of the plateaus, but never for more than a fleeting second had he been able to lift them to see the jagged, white
peaks stand out against the sky. For a bearer marches bent
over at an angle of forty-five degrees.

Chuan looked, then, upon the jagged, white peaks. The
mountains ceased to form the infernally hostile world to
which a bearer must return over and over again in order to
make his wretched living; they seemed now like the immobile waves of a majestic white ocean, tinged here and there
with rose and blue lights. Chuan no longer saw the caravan
pass by or wondered whether one of the ghostly figures
would come to a halt before him; the caravan and its ghostly
figures had gone out of his mind. The cold had dangerously

invaded his thin, ill protected body, but he did not feel either the cold or the bite of the wind on his parchmentlike skin. Only the great snowy waves rolled over and penetrated him. By now he was lying alongside his load, flat on the ground. For a long moment he closed his eyes, and when he opened them he saw the sky filled with birds.

The infinite depth of the sky was pale blue and absolutely cloudless, and the wild geese, flying at a single level, cut it horizontally in two. There were dozens and dozens of groups of birds, all of them in chevron or V formation, flying straight from north to south. As far as Chuan could see, the birds filled the sky, flying in the rarefied air high above the mountain pass. The air was so clear that Chuan could make out every bird, every neck outstretched parallel to the one next to it and every pair of wings making the same regular, powerful rowing motion. Although the wind was blowing from the south and the geese were flying against it, their pace was faultlessly even. Each chevron was like a compass, with unequally long legs; the compasses were all open at exactly the same angle, but without rigidity. They might be compared, also, to large, lightweight, flexible kites, pulled by invisible strings in the same direction.

The rays of the setting sun lit up the ranks of wild geese from below, and those on the western side seemed to be of a lighter color than the rest, a pale gray very close to white. Chuan knew their exact shading, for as a child he had watched them go by, once in spring and once at the end of summer. At dawn he had seen them fly low over the plains, and occasionally his father had got him out of bed at night and led him into the dark and silent fields in order that he might hear the strange whirring noise produced by the beat of thousands of wings. Sometimes, he remembered, the noise had continued for hours on end, and long after he had gone back to bed the geese were still flying over.

How many years had gone by since these dawn and midnight vigils? How long had it been since the stooped caravan bearer had looked up to see the great migration of the graylag geese, high in the sky? All this time the birds had continued, at the same seasons, to fly over. The bearer's body had become more and more bent, and turned into a rag more miserable than the rags which covered it; the insectlike steps he took under his killing load were increasingly jerky, and his hoarse breathing was very painful to the ear. And yet the movement of the birds was just what it had been before. Now the intermediate period of time was contracted and wiped out, and the birds' motion seemed to Chuan like a part of himself which had been preserved from age and poverty and degradation. A great peace came over him. Probably none of the bearers or the men who were leading the horses through the wind-swept pass had noticed that the flight of the geese had begun. Only Chuan, to all appearances a still, parchment-skinned mummy, discolored by the icy cold, but delivered forever of the crushing load it had been his lot to carry, was aware of what was going on. As long as he liked, he would gaze upon this unparalleled sight, yes, just as long as the child Chuan, for whom the passage of time had no meaning.

The graylag geese were flying over the Tien Shan Mountains; soon they would cross the Desert of Takla Makan, the wild Altyn Tagh, the stifling Tibetan plateau and finally, at an altitude of twenty-six thousand feet, the Himalayas, which no other migrant birds are known to pass. Just now their first line was passing over the Muzart Pass, above the only human face turned in their direction, the face of a miserable caravan bearer, whose stare was gradually congealing. Chuan's eyes no longer moved, but he could still see the passage of the great flexible kites overhead. The sky was beginning to darken, but still the wild geese flew over. Their great flight across the high heaven was the last movement registered by the retinas of the poor bearer, who had for so long bent nearly double over the ground.

2

The wild geese had flown from Lake Chany, in the Baraba steppe of western Siberia.

It is difficult to imagine one who all his life long has never seen a stone, or even a pebble; and yet many such men and women live in this part of the world, and most of them know no other. The few, widely scattered villages are composed of wooden houses, and between them there stretches an expanse of flat land as boundless as the sea. For centuries, only forests of pine and birch broke the monotony; the great, grassy swamps were indistinguishable from the land around them. In winter all was mantled in snow; in spring there came an outburst of prairie flowers. Today, many of the swamps have been reclaimed, and periodically through the year the landscape shows animation. In places far removed one from another, long lines of tractors belonging to the Ural-Yenisei Agricultural Collective advance on a wide front, dragging large multiple plows, which prepare the loose, black, extraordinarily fertile soil for sowing. Then, months later, come the harvesters. But even these activities are far separated. In the vast open spaces man, even with his machines, is no more than a tiny, nibbling insect.

Toward the west, at 55 degrees of latitude, lies Lake

Chany, with an area of some thirteen hundred square miles and a maximum depth of thirty feet. Lake Chany is one of the largest preserves of both land and water birds. Over most of its area, and particular in the southeast, where the rivers pour in, a series of long, narrow parallel peninsulas, covered with grass, reeds, and nettles, jut out into the lake and divide it into something like compartments. The peninsulas are themselves sectioned by trenches, lanes of quivering water. Nowhere is there a rock or stone or pebble. The union of earth and water, the marriage of the two elements is as intimate as when, after the Flood, the land, still damp and dripping, offered itself to the view of Noah's dove.

This means that at the beginning of every spring the lake teems with life. Billions of infusorians, grubs and larvae float in the water or stir in the mud, while clouds of insects hover above it. Myriads of wingless insects, batrachians and small rodents and herbivorous and carnivorous animals crowd the shores. Palmipeds nest in the tall reeds, while the insect-eating swallows and the hunting and fishing birds cleave the air. All these creatures, and numberless others which I have failed to name, feed on the dense vegetation, the grains and grasses, on everything that floats and proliferates in the water and everything that crawls and walks on the ground or flies in the air. The various species live off one another, and the mingling of earth and water, the length of the days and the seasonal heat of this vast, landlocked area, all make for a life cycle of a speed and intensity known in few regions of the globe.

And yet, if you walk about in the vicinity of Lake Chany, you see practically nothing. You see swift birds winging their way across the sky and palmipeds flying powerfully along at a lower level, but nothing more. Take a boat, a peasant's punt tied to a stake here or there, and glide along one of the lanes of water between the reeds or six-feet-high walls of nettles, and still you seem to be in solitude. All is in silence, especially in the middle of the day. Now and then a rustle in the grass, the splash of some small animal jumping into the water, the click of a bird's beak, nothing more. By this time you can turn to see you have lost all idea of the direction from which the sound came. All over the world, the same holds true. Even in areas you know well you can go through a woodland thickly populated by squirrels or walk for an hour through brush from which clouds of sparrows will take flight at dawn the next day, without seeing a single living thing. At the approach of man, animals go into silent hiding; and to detect them you must have a cat's patience and keen hearing or, better still, the sense of smell of the dog—that indispensable aid to the hunter. The dog, man's close companion, moves in a world very different from ours, a world of smells of which we have not the faintest conception. And the animals in silent hiding cannot help emitting their characteristic odors, which in moments of fear are intensified and made more perceptible.

Now is the time, then, to follow a dog—this awkward young one, for instance, that we happen to find roaming the southeast shore of Lake Chany, a reddish mongrel with reminiscences of both chow and spaniel. There is no man with him; apparently he is hunting quite on his own, and not very methodically, with his nose at times in the air and at others on the ground, while he wanders from the shore into the water and back to the shore. Now, all of a sudden, he seems to have caught a scent, for he has disappeared among the reeds. . . .

Anatis heard the slight noise made by the dog as he pushed

through the reeds toward her. Birds have a hearing equal to that of man, and the graylag geese are no exception. Anatis was brooding in her nest. The nest was no work of art; it was a rough assemblage of reed stems and branches, held together by mud and lined with soft down which she had plucked with her scaly bill from her own breast. In the nest were six eggs, laid a fortnight before. Within another fortnight, if nothing went wrong, the goslings would be hatched.

Anatis heard the noise among the reeds to her right; she turned her neck slightly to that side, and there was disquiet in her intelligent, light brown eyes. Perhaps you may find ridiculous the idea that feeling of any kind can be expressed by a goose's eye, but that will be only because the only goose you have observed at close range is of the domestic variety. The graylag is the ancestor of the domestic goose, but there is an abyss between his intelligence and that of the fattened denizen of the farmyard. Wild geese are among the most intelligent of birds, and among the most capable of individual behavior.

There was no question, for Anatis, of flying away from the nest and deserting the eggs. And it was wiser not to call for help or make any sound. Perhaps it was only a false alarm. The animal or man—men were scarcely ever seen—who had wandered this way might easily be attracted by some other scent and come upon another nest in the vicinity. This had happened before, when Anatis had followed the development of a whole drama only a short distance away, heard a dog pant and bark, a bird beat its wings and emit a raucous cry. At such times she had not moved. When wild geese are gathered together in large numbers at the various stages of a migration, loyalty is the rule, and sentries alert them to the slightest danger. But here, among the tall reeds, every brooding female or every couple fends for itself, while the others remain silent. No other tactics are possible.

Now the noise was louder, still coming from the right. Raising her head, Anatis saw the tops of the reeds waver and knew that it could not be Anser, her mate, on his way back to the nest. Anser and his fellows, in spite of their bulky bodies, could glide as sinuously as snakes through the tall grass, causing no more than an imperceptible stir. She turned a little so as to face the irruption, if irruption it was to be. The reeds shook from top to bottom directly before her, and then she saw the dog, a shaggy, snub-nosed, short-legged creature.

He was less than a yard away. He looked at the goose in a not unkindly manner, raising and lowering his head as if to verify that he had found the source of the smell which had led him hither.

Anatis leaned forward, slightly opening her wings and making a hissing sound. Her brownish gray neck was like a short, thick snake, and her horny bill with the recurved upper mandible was not exactly reassuring. The dog hesitated, as if he had been taken by surprise. Probably the brooding females which he had come upon before belonged to smaller species. When they did not immediately fly away, he would knock them over, then, if necessary, break their necks and eat them; and afterwards he would devour the eggs, which he liked best.

Finally, heartened by the memory of his previous expeditions, he moved forward and, with an air that was still not unfriendly, started to butt the goose's chest with his nose in order to topple her over. But a nip of her bill just between the eyes caused him to draw back. Anatis stretched her short, snakelike neck as far out as possible and moved it with sur-

prising rapidity from one side to the other, always turning
her horny bill toward the dog. He was beginning to understand that the goose was not to be tumbled over as easily as
a flowerpot.

As soon as he advanced his muzzle in the hope of catching
hold of her neck, the bill came down upon it. Anatis aimed,
purposefully, at his eyes. At intervals he closed them and
whimpered plaintively, then he opened them and tried again
to bite. Then another idea apparently crossed his brain. He
gave up the idea of battling an elusive snake and made a
flank attack, attempting to dig his nose into the goose's left
side. But a formidable blow from the muscled wing discomfited and momentarily thwarted him. When he recovered,
Anatis had turned in the nest and was once more facing him,
her neck stretched out.

As if to bolster up his courage, the dog leaned forward on
his front paws and barked furiously. Anatis gave several
honking calls in reply. It should be remarked that this was
the first time she had used her voice; until now she had only
hissed. At the first premonition of danger she had lain low,
in conformity with the tactics of her kind, and even at the
sight of the dog she had remained silent, perhaps because
she was confident of her defenses. But now that he leaned
forward and barked she too made herself heard. Was this a
purely reflex action, or was she calling Anser?

Wild geese are monogamous, and—rare among birds—their
union lasts not for a single season but their whole life long;
when a goose is bereft of its mate it does not seek another.
Their affection is truly touching to see, and Anatis was used
to having Anser near, as a devoted and helpful companion.
He helped her build the nest, sat on the eggs while she went
to stretch her legs, to eat nettles and grass, to drink and

splash about in the water; on the long journey of migration he flew at her side.

And yet . . . No man can possibly see the world from a bird's point of view, and there is no way of knowing whether Anser was present in Anatis' thoughts when he was physically away, whether, when she was in danger, she was actually able to *think* about him. It would be an anthropomorphical fallacy to say that Anatis was calling Anser as a woman might call her husband in a moment of distress. Still, I cannot admit that the truly touching affection which geese show each other is only a series of mechanical gestures without past or future, leaving no lasting imprint, akin to memory, upon the bird mind, different as it may be from our own. I incline to believe that the call which Anatis made in answer to the dog's barking was an appeal to her mate. It is not by mere chance that I have begun this book about animal migrations, of which so many aspects are still obscure, with a chapter on birds, and that among birds I have first picked out a pair of wild geese. In the course of their story I shall try to tell you with what resemblance to ourselves we can reasonably credit them. Meanwhile let us return to the nest on the shore of Lake Chany.

The excited dog again lunged forward. At the corner of his right eye he received a peck which caused him to howl with pain, but this time he did not draw back. Indeed, he managed to sink his teeth into the lower side of the goose's neck, at the level of the throat. The muscles at the base of the neck, suddenly swollen and taut, resisted the pressure of his teeth above them, but through a mass of feathers the dog could feel flesh, and turning his head to one side he continued to bite into it, while Anatis flailed the air with her great wings in order not to be toppled over. She was unable to lower her head, however hard she tried, and her bill no longer served as a weapon. The growling dog kept his hold and tightened his bite, paralyzing her neck muscles. Anatis could only beat her wings and call out in despair.

Suddenly she perceived a great shadow above her head and felt a weight on her shoulders. Another pair of wings was beating now, and with a brief whine the dog let go. Anser to the rescue! Fresh to the fray, the courageous gander set upon the dog with his bill; and the dog loosened his grip and retreated. Anser was now very much in the fight; and, because he did not have to stick to the nest, he was able to counter-attack, boldly. The angry dog barked and tried to bite him; every now and then his muzzle grazed the gander's breast, but the gander, now hovering in the air, now planting his feet on the ground, drew strategically back or to the side, and then advanced again, thrusting his horny bill at the dog's eyes.

A scientist with a taste for sport, looking on at this match, would have said: "Anser is trying to force a quick victory, but he won't be able to keep up the pace. True, a bird does not expend much effort to stay in the air; but every take-off from ground depletes his energy, and this beating of wings will quickly exhaust him. The dog, being heavier and less mobile, is compelled to take the punishment, but on the other hand without expending much strength. Anser will exhaust himself to the point of asphyxiation—unless he manages to strike a decisive blow."

Anser had not yet struck the dog's eyes, and his movements were obviously slower than before. Anatis saw that she must reenter the fight, and now she did not hesitate to leave her nest. The dog was far too busy to go for the eggs, and there was no danger in leaving them uncovered.

The dog had seized the front edge of one of Anser's wings

when Anatis moved to attack him. His head was immobilized
and made an extremely vulnerable target for her bill. One
nip in the vicinity of the eyes persuaded him to let go of the
feather-covered flesh, whose taste was already in his mouth.
Hardly had he relaxed his jaws when the great wing glided
away toward the ground, then came back up at him with all
the punch of an uppercut. Now two short, powerful snakes,
armed with bills, advanced on him from either side. As the
birds jumped up and down, trying to maneuver him away
from the nest, the beating of their wings caused the feathers
he had torn away to fly. Obviously the dog was no longer
thinking of the eggs. He barked, growled, and whined under
the pressure put upon him by the pair of graylag geese. At
times he whined for several minutes on end, as if it had been
all a mistake to throw himself into this adventure. Whining,
he gave ground, shaking his head as if there were wasps
about it. Then, all of a sudden, he shied to one side, turned
and silently disappeared behind the reeds.

Three seconds later he stuck his head and chest out of the
tall grass and barked, but without advancing. Anatis rested
on her eggs, while Anser stood between her and the dog with
his wings half open and a hissing came out of his throat. He
made as if to move forward, and the dog once more disappeared. Anatis and Anser saw the tops of the reeds move,
farther and farther and farther away, in the direction of the
lake, and heard the clump of his big, awkward paws on the
muddy shore. Probably the dog had found another scent to
follow.

3

For Anatis and Anser, the combat just described was the
most notable event of the season immediately preceding the

long flight to the south. They were about twelve years old. Graylag geese, like the other Lamellirostres (birds with a hard, scaly bill), have a long life span—longer, some authors say, than that of either crows or parrots. The established records are a hundred years for a barnacle goose and two hundred for a swan.

Anser and Anatis therefore may be considered as a young couple. Although born on the damp shores of Lake Chany, they had met and paired two thousand miles away, in the great Ganges valley. This was where the graylag geese landed every year after flying over the Tien Shan Mountains, the Desert of Takla Makan, the high plateaus of Tibet, and the Himalayas. Anser and Anatis were then only a few months old, and this was the first time they had gone on the great flight.

In early autumn, when the birds arrived, the weather was still warm. The green plain, still soft and wet from the summer downpours, was drying off in the last gusts of the southwesterly monsoons. After the rain stopped completely, the air was cool and dry, and the sun shone all day long. It was at the end of this agreeably temperate winter that Anser, although still sexually immature, felt the need of finding a mate, or more exactly a fiancée. This word, as we shall see, describes exactly what he was seeking.

The graylag geese of the great valley lived in closely knit family groups. Several times a day, Anser's family, like the others, left its own particular place and went to feed and flit about in a neutral area, half land, half water, where birds of every kind walked, swam, and flew together. One morning, near the river, Anser saw a young goose walking with her family. With her brownish gray plumage—dark brown in the center of the back and white toward the tail—she differed

from her brothers only in the size of her body and the deli-
cacy of her head and bill and from her sisters not at all; in
short, she might have been any one of the thousands of young
female graylag geese that peopled the valley; and yet . . .

Anser left his own group, took a few steps in her direction,
and halted. Perhaps he had noticed that the suitors who
came too close were chased away by either the father or the
father and mother together. A runaway match, or anything
remotely like it, is severely frowned upon by a wild-goose
family. It was up to him to propose from a respectful distance. Taking his stance some twenty steps away, Anser
threw a quite explicit look in Anatis' direction. (Yes, this was
Anatis, and no other!) She did not so much as return his
glance, but her parents examined him somewhat severely.
Anser began to strut from one side to the other, still at a
certain distance, continuing to eye Anatis, to straighten his
neck and stick out his chest, as if to call attention to the way
he carried himself.

This little demonstration, or parade, as naturalists call it,
was not particularly impressive. Certain male birds appeal to
the female by unfolding their many-colored, iridescent wings;
they puff up and raise their whole plumage, open the tail into
a fan, and otherwise make themselves fascinating and irresistible. The buzzard performs acrobatic feats in the air; the
white-faced tern makes his beloved the gift of a fish, and the
Antarctic penguin that of a symbolic pebble. The bowerbird,
which is related to the birds of paradise, builds a miniature
arbor of twigs, arranges in front of it fruit and flowers which
he replaces as often they wilt or fade, and a collection of
small objects—feathers, bones, shells, and stones—whose colors
harmonize with his own, then points them out, one by
one, to the female's admiring gaze. The albatross, on the

other hand, simply exhibits the enormous spread of his wings. It is not surprising that every bird should show off his most spectacular attractions. Anser, who had neither brilliant plumage nor extraordinary physical prowess to display, possessed the hereditary virtue of family devotion, and he was intent upon attracting the attention of his loved one and winning the approval of her severely scrutinizing parents.

Just then a young male of another family, who either was attracted by the goings-on or happened to be passing by, came upon the scene. Anser hissed and threw himself upon him, pecking wildly. The intruder first made as if to flee before the attack, then changed his mind, turned around, and accepted the challenge. This was doubtless Anser's first fight; heretofore he had enjoyed a sheltered life in the bosom of his family. Now, however quiet a young gander he had been before, he fought fiercely, as if aware that his whole matrimonial project was at stake. He made as much noise as possible, in order to draw his loved one's attention, whereas his adversary, who did not have the same reason to be brave, brought much less energy into play and in two minutes acknowledged his defeat. He turned around and ran away, making a pitifully plaintive sound, while Anser honked his victory. He saw that the young female was glancing at him now, briefly, but just as meaningfully as he had looked at her. His suit was a success. He honked a few moments longer, looking around in vain for another adversary. But there was no need to fight again, for now the loved one was honking almost as loudly as he. The next thing he knew, she was walking toward him, and her parents did not make the least objection. The betrothal had followed straight upon the proposal, and now the ceremony was over. The two walked away, side by side. They would live together, as chastely as brother and sister, for sixteen months to come.

Among some birds the parade immediately precedes the actual mating; others parade not only then but also at the moment of choice. It is interesting to note that the most dazzling parades go with the briefest union. The male and female grouse, both of them decked out in splendor, parade together, each for the benefit of the other. They swell their necks, let their wings droop, raise and spread their tails, at the same time whistling, cooing, and vibrating their feathers. And what of the marriage that follows this vain show? It does not last for a single minute after the act of reproduction.

Anser and Anatis lived devotedly together in the great valley; and when spring came they took their place in the cloud of birds which flew northward again, to Lake Chany. There they lived all the next season as fiancés, untroubled by the amorous maneuvers of the couples around them, by the numberless unions which were consummated, not too discreetly, in the tall reeds along the shore. In the autumn they flew again to the Ganges valley, then once more back to the north. This time Anser and Anatis knew each other and procreated. And so they did every succeeding year.

4

North, south, east, and west of Lake Chany, all over the vast steppe, the rectangular fields of golden grain rippled in the summer breezes, with thousands upon thousands of warbling larks rising vertically above them. Then came the battle front of gigantic threshing and harvesting machines of the Ural-Yenisei Agricultural Collective, leaving a cloud of chaff over an expanse of stubble. These were followed by an army of trucks, which loaded sacks of wheat and bales of straw. Then all the machines went away, and the steppe again became an infinite stretch of flat land, studded with forests of pine and birch and, along the river, occasional clusters of wooden houses where the silence of evening was broken by the song of a harmonica. The days were still long and warm, under a pale blue sky. At high noon, everything was magnificently still; there was no feeling of oppression, but only a great harmony between air and soil, a peaceful rest in the day's work. Oh, to lie perfectly quiet, not even to think, but simply to let one's eyes follow the tiny cumulus cloud that gradually disintegrates as it drifts across the sky! . . .

Meanwhile, among the reeds by the lake shore, anxiety reigned. Perhaps this is too strong a word, but there is no other. Anser, Anatis, and the other wild geese of Lake Chany were not harassed by anxiety of a human kind. But if you had been able to pass as invisibly as the breeze over the lanes of water and the tall grass and look down into the clearings that studded this watery kingdom, you would have seen that among the goose families, which at this hour should have been peacefully napping with head tucked under wing, something out of the ordinary was astir, and the harmony between them and their peaceful surroundings was broken. The graylag geese were pacing up and down and then halting abruptly; whole families left their dwellings and gathered in a wide open space, where they seemed to be waiting for something, then they went back to their nests, only to return to the meeting place. They looked at one another in silence, with an air of restlessness. Restlessness perhaps describes their condition more accurately than anxiety.

Somewhere within each bird, in its brain or glands or some

other hidden part, an irresistible impulse had been born, an impulse to fly south. The time had come; Anser and Anatis, and all the other wild geese who had ever flown to the Ganges delta, knew it, and so did thousands of young geese who had never made the flight. If, as naturalists have done, you had captured one of these, separated it from its parents, and shut it up in a cage or other enclosure, it too would have paced up and down with a restless look in its eye when the time came. The irresistible impulse is communicated to whole species, and even a bird that has never migrated feels it.

In the autumn, with the arrival of the migrating season, swallows assemble, and after a few group trial flights start for their winter home to the south. Warblers, goldfinches, redstarts, and numberless other birds scattered over the countryside weld themselves into a fast-flying cloud. The stork rises almost vertically, like a helicopter, and, having taken its bearings, rows with unerring aim to its destination. The albatross takes flight from a rock, spreads its incomparable wings over the sea, and navigates on upsweeping air currents, like a glider.

But our graylag geese could not fly.

Provident Nature, which warns each of these birds that the still beauty of the summer must have an end and that in order not to be surprised by the arctic cold they must, by mid-August, start toward the south, at the same time plays a miserable trick upon them. This is also the molting season, and the wings which should carry them through the sky are completely useless.

And so, on the shores of Lake Chany, this August day was one of silent agitation. From hour to hour larger numbers of birds congregated restlessly together. When night came they squatted on the ground, without sleeping. Twenty times an

hour they got up, paced up and down, turned their heads
from side to side and listened nervously. Everywhere a humming, gently scraping, and sliding sound seemed to indicate
the assembly of a dumb, invisible crowd upon the lake's
south shore. And such an assembly was actually taking
place.

Well before dawn, every one of the long, narrow peninsulas in the vicinity of the tributary rivers was covered with
wild geese; and they continued to arrive from the north, east,
and west shores by water and land, in ever increasing numbers. Another dusk and another night descended upon them.
Then, as if at a signal, the crowd of geese with a single impulse began to move toward the south. They paddled across
the waterways and pushed through the dense vegetation,
without an outcry, all heading in the same direction, and each
family keeping together.

The front line of the great army reached the edge of the
vegetation. A few more clumps of reeds, of tall grass and
nettles, and then nothing but the great open spaces. There
was no moon, and the dim light of the stars revealed only a
small part of the steppe, which extended to right and left
and before them. Only the stars indicated the points of the
compass, and wild geese do not look at the stars. Nevertheless the front line advanced toward the south. The wild
geese of Lake Chany, the powerful flyers that had gone over
the Himalayas, the Altyn Tagh, the Tien Shan Mountains,
had begun their great exodus on foot.

5

In many parts of the globe birds change their habitat at
the approach of bad weather. Searching for more agreeable

living conditions, they betake themselves to climes with which hereditary experience has made them acquainted. The two preceding statements, which you may have taken at their face value, are a brief and inexact description of the phenomenon of migration. Birds do not pursue the sun, like well-to-do winter visitors to the Riviera. For one thing, even within a well defined region, they do not all migrate when winter comes. And if there is such a thing as hereditary experience, how has it been formed?

I believe that the least tedious way of tackling this enigma is to listen to the scientists who have argued and still argue about it. Without reproducing their discussions—some of which fill volumes—I shall summarize them as accurately as I can. Let us imagine that we have gathered at a round table a group of scientists willing to set forth their opinions and hypotheses in condensed form. Although these are of various dates including the contemporary, we are totally uninformed, and so the chronology does not matter. I propose to designate the speakers by names which are in one way or another attached to their theories.

Professor *Eocene.*—In order to find the origin and cause of bird migrations, we must go back to the Flood and even beyond. At the end of the Tertiary period and the beginning of the Mesozoic era, the earth's climate was much warmer than it is today, and the seasons much less sharply differentiated. At this time birds had no reason to migrate, living in a comparatively even climate the year around. Then, little by little, for various and complex reasons, the earth's temperature began to decrease. Certain mammals started to move to lower latitudes, and others, slower or more resistant, protected themselves against the cold with a coat of fur. As for the birds, which were able to travel more easily, they "followed the sun" in a series of slow stages, so that they were always in a sufficiently warm climate, which afforded them their customary food. However, in obedience to the biological law by virtue of which every living being remains attached to its birthplace, they learned to return every year to their place of origin, as soon as the weather permitted. After a number of years, it became a habit.

Professor *Nenni.*—In this case, why are not all birds migratory? Why are so many species sedentary, and others half sedentary, half migrant? In the light of this theory, how does my eminent colleague explain the behavior of the Corvidae through the ages? Spread today over most of the globe, they migrate little. And the most sedentary member of this family, *Corvus Corax,* or raven, is to be found in the Arctic zone! And there are other sedentary birds in the polar region: the great white owl, the ptarmigan, the ivory gull, Ross's gull . . . Obviously these birds have adapted themselves to their environment, however few its attractions. Why, then, have others preferred migration to adaptation? Or, if you wish to put it the other way, why have those mentioned preferred adapting themselves to migrating? A theory which has so many exceptions doesn't seem to me to hold water.

Professor *Thermos.*—My thesis is analogous to that of Professor Eocene, but in a way contrary to it. I believe that the migratory birds of today came originally from the most temperate parts of the globe, and that at a comparatively recent epoch, geologically speaking—that is, after the postglacial period—they extended their habitat to colder climes. In bad weather, they simply return to their place of origin.

Professor *Nenni.*—That's just as questionable an explanation as the one before. I insist that, if it were only a matter of climate, the present-day migrants could have just as easily achieved adaptation. So many other animals have achieved it!

Professor *Eocene.*—But, for birds, it's so much easier to fly away!

Professor *Nenni.*—Then why don't they fly away as soon as they start to lack food or suffer from the cold? Many birds deprived by some natural cataclysm of their food, or exposed to the freezing cold of an unusually early and severe winter, have stayed where they were, simply because the migrating season had not yet arrived. Some of them starved or froze to death. And why, on the other hand, when the exact time has come, do birds start to migrate, even if there are still ideal conditions around them?

Professor *Eocene.*—Hereditary memory prods them, and this memory has been formed by a general rule rather than accidental exceptions. Birds have acquired the habit of starting in time because over the course of the ages those who didn't do it perished. It's a matter of natural selection.

Professor *Nenni.*—Very well; then, explain the case of the first migrant. What warned him that his food was going to give out and he risked dying of cold? And how was he to know that he would find a more favorable climate somewhere else? In our day, a wave of unusual cold doesn't cause any sedentary birds to migrate. They stay where they are, and paleonotology teaches us that those who don't adapt simply die on the spot, without attempting to fly away.

Professor *Cosmos.*—It's true that this theory of the search for an eternal springtime rests on a very shaky foundation. In my view, migration is not an act of will. The migratory bird is swept away by a cosmic current so powerful that he cannot possibly oppose it. Every change of season is marked by important physical, electrical, and magnetic phenomena, and the bird is subjected to a galvanotropic urge, which permeates every cell of his body and impels him, quite irresistibly, to fly away. These magnetic phenomena precede the change of temperature, and that is why he has an impulse to migrate before the cold or heat actually descends upon him. And this same galvanotropism not only sparks his departure, but also directs him.

The other professors, together.—Yes, dear colleague, you've set forth your theory of galvanotropism before, with the same enthusiasm and the same lack of proofs. We think it's daring and highly poetic, nothing more.

Professor *Lejour*.—I haven't yet had a chance to speak. In my opinion, migratory birds are subject to the influence of light. The experiments of Rowan and Wolfson prove that the increase of light radiation in the spring stimulates the activity of the bird's sexual glands and hence a need for movement, which causes him to fly away. By submitting birds to artificial light during the winter months, these two scientists provoked a premature migration.

Professor *Nenni*.—This doesn't explain the repetition of the same urge in autumn. Moreover, castrated birds are known to migrate along with the rest.

Professor *Complex*.—Recent scientific research seems to indicate that light doesn't act directly upon the sexual glands, but rather upon the pituitary body. A change in metabolism is the determining factor of both spring and autumn migrations.

Professor *Nenni*.—This is all very complicated. It doesn't explain why variations in the intensity or duration of light should cause some birds to migrate while others remain indifferently at home. And many species feel the spring migratory impulse even though their habitat is near the equator, where the length of the day hardly varies from one end of the year to the other.

At this point we may end the discussion. The latest research does make it appear that the migratory impulse is caused by a modification of neuro-endocrine activity. This modification, which is produced by the action of certain glands, notably the thyroid, causes the bird to react to certain subtle cosmic variations, too subtle perhaps for us to detect them. And if these variations do not affect non-migrant birds, it is because their neuro-endocrine activity does not suffer the same fluctuations. This, in brief, is the mechanism, and the one that works not only upon birds but upon all migratory animals. Shall we ever completely understand it? "It is very rare," writes Maeterlinck, "for any mystery to disappear entirely. Usually, it only changes place. But it is important and desirable to bring about this change."

6

Along with tens of thousands of other wild geese, Anser, Anatis, and their young walked toward the south. They formed a huge army, divided into regiments of unequal size, marching more silently than any human counterpart. Other equally large formations came after, at a distance such that they could not see the leaders, but followed, on their own initiative and unhesitatingly, in the same direction. Streams flow from far-away mountains into the rivers and lakes of the steppe, or are absorbed by its marshes. The army swam across them and then continued on foot on the opposite shore.

A breeze had come up out of the southwest. After about four hours of marching, there was a slight stir among the

group around Anser and Anatis, or rather a gradual slackening of pace, together with an almost imperceptible veering
to the left. The birds of the advance guard were aware that a
halting place was at hand. Soon after this, the terrain became increasingly uneven. The geese heard leaves rustle in
the breeze and felt a touch of dampness in the air. Trees
emerged from the darkness, first scattered and then in clumps
and groves, until the geese found themselves in a forest,
whose foliage partially concealed the starry sky. In the midst
of birches, the regiment came to a stop, and the birds flat-
tened themselves out on the damp ground. The halting place
was admirably adapted to their purpose, which was to lie
low during the daylight hours and resume their march the
next evening.

The village was barely visible in the darkness; it was a collection of primitive, wooden houses, unevenly disposed
along the river, which for centuries had known nothing new.
In other places, far away, the world might be changing. But
in the isbas a gun hanging on the wall, or perhaps a harmonica, was the only sign of life, of the fact that, in spite of everything, this wooden village, too, was floating down the stream
of Time.

That night the men had not taken down their guns. To
fire them in the darkness would mean to risk killing one another. Every one of the villagers wore a knife on his belt and
carried a club in his right hand while the left was free to
hold a dog on a leash. Every night for the last week the peasants had ventured out onto the steppe. On the preceding
nights, the dogs had done nothing but sniff the ground in-
conclusively, first to one side and then to the other. Now
they were straining at their leashes, all in the same direction,
toward the north. Whenever any one of them barked, he was

hit over the head; and then he contented himself with an excited whimper. The peasants were forced to break into a run as they let the animals pull them along.

The grassy plain stretched out like a borderless lake under the starlit sky, broken here and there by islands of bushes. The dogs tugged at their leashes with growing excitement, and more and more frequent beating was necessary in order to prevent them from barking. Suddenly the villagers who had gone farthest ahead called out:

"There they are!"

At some distance, perhaps a hundred yards away, the dark ground seemed to move, as if its immobile surface had suddenly been transformed into a mass of ripples, advancing along a straight front toward the hunters. Now there was no way to stop the dogs from barking. The men ran after them, and when they let go the leashes the dogs shot forward like arrows. The peasants knew that the mass of wild geese had no more time in which to change direction; that there were more birds than they could possibly kill, even if the ranks were split by terror.

Their clubs came down not on the dogs, but on the geese. A goose's neck and wings are so solid as to resist the blows of a club, and the best way to stop one is to break its webbed foot. But, in the darkness, the peasants laid about them in haphazard fashion, with all their strength. When one could catch hold of a bird he held it between his legs and bled it with the knife. Then he got up and once more wielded his club, attached by a thong to his wrist. Every now and then one of them was nipped by a bird's bill, but under the joint attack of men and barking dogs and the pressure of their companions surging from behind, the geese were too thoroughly demoralized to defend themselves with skill. As members of a vast crowd pressing toward the south they were much less able to fight back than they would have been either alone or in couples, outside the migrating season. The great army moved at night in order to avoid the attack of birds of prey, their traditional enemies, and this nocturnal assault of human beings was unforeseen and bewildering. Perhaps men had not lived long enough on the steppe for the memory of their yearly attacks to be imprinted on the hereditary memory of the species.

The men were panting and sweating, but they did not relax for a single moment in their intent to bludgeon the birds and cut their throats. The prospect of salting away a supply of meat for the coming winter was not the only thing that inspired them. The excitement of the slaughter, which made the dogs bark until they were positively choking, was working upon them in almost the same manner, until every one of them was a devil incarnate, set upon killing the greatest possible number of birds. The flapping of wings and raucous cries of distress served only to excite them further; sometimes they cut themselves on their own knives and then licked their wounded hands, like animals, simultaneously licking the blood of the geese, with which their hands were covered. A moment later, forgetful of their wounds, they recommenced laying about them. The only evidence of the fact that they had not entirely lost their reason was that they took care not to lurch too close to one another, in order to avoid having their own throats cut. Actually, they did not have to move far, in one direction or another. The army of wild geese continued to advance, pouring around them like the successive waves of a flood.

By the time the whole mass of birds had flowed by, leaving the killers surrounded by an expanse of once more im-

mobile ground, the stars had begun to pale in the sky. The
killers staggered among the corpses, knife in hand, wandering off to hack at an occasional pair of wings which seemed
to be still flapping.

Anser, Anatis, and their brood had escaped the slaughter.
The piles of feathered bodies, which the peasants would
shortly divide among them, did not represent the fiftieth
part of the marching army. Other sections, to the right and
left, had not found any killers in their path. Night after night
they moved southward across the steppe, on an irregular
front some five miles wide. The regiment to which Anser and
Anatis belonged marched for ten consecutive nights in this
fashion, covering over a hundred miles. At the end of the
tenth night the birds detected the smell of water ahead, a
smell that grew progressively stronger. They were approaching the band of vegetation around Lake Kulunda, south-
southeast of their point of departure.

In the light of the rising sun the body of water appeared
before them, gleaming like a mirror among the tall grass.
They threw themselves eagerly into it, and soon a large area
was entirely covered with birds, splashing intoxicatedly
about in order to shake off the dust of the steppe. A large
part of the migrating army met upon these shores. In the
immediate neighborhood there were no villagers, no plowed
fields; the weather was fair, and the atmosphere one of perfect peace. That day thousands of families enjoyed a deep
sleep.

The geese did not set out again that night, nor for two
nights following. They stayed together, standing motionless
on their feet a great part of the time and observing one another, in the same way as they had done at Lake Chany.
Only now they were not so restless. A dozen times an hour

they painstakingly ran their bills over their feathers. Along the back edge of the wings the powerful remiges had grown in, and attained normal development. They had grown in on thousands and thousands of birds simultaneously, like blades of wheat sprouting in the same field.

On the fourth day, when the white sky of dawn had turned pale blue and there was a streak of pink on the horizon, the wild geese were still spread out around the lake. The characteristic cheeping of small birds rose from the vegetation. At intervals of barely more than a second, families of geese took off into the air, rose to a certain height, flew in a slightly wavering line over the water, with beaks and necks outstretched and feet pulled in, and then circled and came back to the ground. Anser, Anatis, and their brood all made this trial flight.

To the east the sky was increasingly rosy, but the geese flew about for a full hour before sunrise. Then, as if at an order from an invisible control tower, all wings ceased moving, and the birds stood, almost motionless, on the ground. Suddenly the sun shot like an arrow over the horizon; the rosy tint changed to flaming red, and the pale sky overhead to a deeper blue. Abruptly a single goose rose into the air. In the light of dawn its brownish gray plumage was black and white as it hovered, shimmering, above the tall grass. Already it was not alone, for the signal had been given. For several seconds the grass and reeds were shaken and bent by a powerful downward movement of the air, as if fifty helicopters had left the ground together. With landing gear drawn up, one group of birds rose above another, keeping the sun on their left side. The mass of them spread out indefinitely, to left and right. Already flexible parallel lines, several miles long, were flying straight toward the south, while all around Lake Kulunda other clouds of birds rose up to follow.

Anser and Anatis, with their goslings at either side, kept their place in the front line, rowing through the calm air with a rhythm of eight wingbeats to a second. The flying squadron's speed was more than forty miles an hour.

This is not a particularly impressive figure. For a long time migratory birds were credited with much greater speeds; but measurement with apparatus in airplanes during the last fifteen years has provided some definitive figures. The cruising speed of wild geese and ducks is from forty-four to fifty-six miles an hour; that of plovers from forty to fifty; that of swallows, from thirty-seven to fifty. Numerous small birds navigate at twenty-five, thirty and thirty-five miles an hour. At need, all these birds can fly faster; some, much faster. A swallow on the chase may reach seventy-five miles an hour; a wild goose under attack, nearly seventy. Peregrine falcons can descend upon their prey at a hundred and fifty miles an hour, and in America one has been clocked at a hundred and eighty, a world record—achieved, to be sure, in the course of a nose dive. Under ordinary conditions, birds are not daredevil flyers. In normal migration flight they save their strength, and travel at a moderate speed.

The squadron flew over the plain in open formation, at an altitude of twenty-three hundred feet. No man has seen or will ever see the world as a bird sees it, but we may be sure that at this height no detail of the country below escaped Anser's sight. The bird's eye has special provision for receiving color sensations and light contrasts that man cannot take in.

"Calling all pilots! We shall now follow the valley of this tributary of the Irtysh River, just there in front of you and

running in an almost exactly north-south direction. At the
signal, you will wheel and at the same time rise to an altitude
of forty-five hundred feet. The front line is to break into V
formations. I repeat: At the signal, break into V formations
and start to rise. Signal!"

There is really nothing either ridiculous or arbitrary about
this interpretation of the gabbling noise, which sounded with
peculiar intensity at the moment when the squadron reached
the opening of the first valley. Many ornithologists believe
or suppose that wild geese communicate their observations
or flying orders to one another by gabbling. When gabbling
grows louder, a change of route almost invariably follows, as
if the geese were connected by a radio system.

The long parallel lines of the squadron began to break at
intervals, like thread cut into sections by a pair of scissors.
The space between the sections widened and then, in a simple, miraculously natural movement without any loss of
speed, each section thrust a point forward and turned into a
great flexible kite, with two legs, which opened at the rear.
The whole sky was filled with V formations, made up of birds
rowing with unfailingly regular strokes through the air. All
at the same time, the V's rose and drew nearer together, until
the entire squadron took the elongated form of an aerial
river, adapted to the shape of the valley.

A straight front line had been well suited to flight over the
wide spaces of the steppe. But the geese knew that the moun-
tainous territory they were now approaching would bring
all sorts of disturbances in the air, which they must be prepared to meet. Their aerial river traveled along directly
above the earthly one, and the V formation was intended to
prevent the birds from disturbing one another by any irregu-
larity of motion. Each group flew through a quiet alley, as if

it were accomplishing the migration alone. From time to time, the bird at the point of each V shifted to one side and let the other members pass, falling in at the end of one of the legs while one of his fellows took his place. There is no explanation for this behavior, and aerodynamic experiments have proved that the post of group leader is no more tiring than any other.

That day the squadron flew for ten hours consecutively, at an even speed of forty-four miles an hour. At times the aerial river gained or lost altitude, expanded or compressed its width, according to the variations of the terrain below. After nine hours of flight the gabbling once more increased in volume; and a little later a blue line appeared, beyond a ripple of glazed hills, on the distant horizon. Stretching from east to west, it seemed like the line of the ocean. Actually, it was another lake, so large that the neighboring Kirghizes do not call it Lake Balkhash; they simply call it "the sea." It has an area of more than seven thousand square miles, and the reeds on its shores grow to a height of sixteen feet. Here the birds rested for several days.

7

Take an atlas and open it to the planisphere pages. Place the point of your pencil north of Labrador, at any point you choose of Baffin Land. Beginning there, draw a broken line through Newfoundland, Pernambuco, Rio de Janeiro, Buenos Aires, to the middle of the pampas of Argentina. This line represents the traject of the ninety-three-hundred-mile autumnal migration of the American golden plover, which in the spring fearlessly embarks upon the homeward journey. His cousin, the golden plover of the Pacific, covers the distance of twenty-five hundred miles between Alaska and Hawaii without a single stop on the way. You may follow in the same fashion the European storks and swallows all the way to South Africa. In the Antarctic region, in autumn terns are found which were born in the north of Europe only a few months before.

Then are we to consider the two thousand miles covered by the wild geese as a mediocre achievement? At this point we must draw upon our imagination. We must raise ourselves above the earth's crust, even higher than a stratospheric plane, to the height attained by certain rockets, which have brought back photographs of continental areas so vast that they include a curve of the globe. The relief of the region over which the wild geese fly is fantastic and positively terrifying in character. No other part of the earth reveals anything like this chaotic block of overlapping folds, which we know as mountain ranges. This is the difficult route the wild geese must follow; for us, it is easy enough to cover it in our thoughts within something like four minutes.

The first barrier, stretching octopuslike tentacles in every direction, is that of the Tien Shan range of which I have already spoken, with its highest peak, the Khan Tengri or King of the Heavens, more than 23,600 feet high. Beyond this is an oval depression, reaching from east to west, the Desert of Takla Makan, which is a prolongation of the Gobi Desert. Next comes a gigantic block in which there is no interruption: the Altyn Tagh, whose principal summit is called the Mountain of Darkness. The tortuous chain of the Tien Shan is dwarfed by this vast assembly of 23,000-foot peaks, covered with snow the year round above the 14,000-foot line. Another similar range, the Ustun Tagh, follows close upon it, and then tiers of colossal glaciers lead to what geographers call the plateau of Tibet, where the average altitude is 16,000 feet. Here there is almost absolute solitude; on the greater part of these 300,000 square miles no human being has ever set foot. Only a few trails are ever traveled, and the only habitations are lamaseries, which stand out on the rocky mountain sides, hundreds of miles apart. Once the short summer is gone, an angry blast of west wind howls through the vast, empty spaces, with growing intensity, all through the day. Only at night does it die down, giving way to a greater wind from the north and to a sinister silence. Even in summer, there are frequent hailstorms.

Beyond the plateau lie the Himalayas. Following their south-southeasterly course, the migrants approached this last barrier at the north face of the great mass of Chomo-Lungma, better known today as Mount Everest.

The birds had flown in stages of 160 to 220 miles a day, except for the extra effort of crossing, without pause, the 300-mile Takla Makan Desert. The army had split up along the way, for none of the mountain resting places could have contained it. Most of the time they slept in wide, barren spaces, crowding behind any rise in the terrain which afforded some degree of shelter. As soon as they resumed their flight they were buffeted by the wind. A bird standing on the ground offers the wind the same sort of target as a leafy bush, and is visibly shaken. But, once it has taken off, it is plunged into the displaced air and is like a swimmer in a swift current, which carries him on or holds him back without interfering with his movements: he is aware only of a sharp acceleration or deceleration and of the swirl of an eddy about him. The groups took the air, one after another, gained altitude, separated into chevrons and set their course in a south-southeasterly direction. Occasionally birds of prey caused an alarm to be sounded; some geese fell prey to their attacks and others dropped out or disappeared for no good reason. But the total losses were small in proportion to the size of the great flying army.

As they went along, their halts became briefer and briefer, on account of the precarious nature of the stopping places, swept by high winds and covered with ice and snow. At the height of their mountain crossing, the rarity of the atmosphere increased the fatigue of flying, but they never let up their speed. Each bird must have felt that the goal was near. Anser, Anatis, and their brood flew in the same V-formation group as before, crossing over the bristling mountain peaks at an altitude of nearly 20,000 feet. Anatis was occupying the post of group leader, and flying as powerfully as any male of the species. The night was totally black, but above the invisible earth the squadron moved south-southeast, without a single degree of deviation.

Here we are at the heart of the enigma: how are these winged migrants guided?

Dr. K. S. Lashley and Professor J. B. Watson, of Baltimore, took young terns from the Gulf of Mexico, banded them for identification and carried them over the water, in closed cages, 250 miles from their place of origin. They returned unerringly to it. Professor Wodzicki took two storks by plane all the way from Poland to Lydda, in Palestine, a distance of 1,350 miles, with the same result. Numerous other experiments have confirmed the existence of this "homing instinct."

The directional assurance of migratory birds is still more amazing. For a long time people were content with the following explanation: "Birds are endowed with vision and topographical memory of an extraordinary character. After they have flown once or twice over a certain itinerary, they can follow it by certain landmarks on the earth below: rivers, lakes, valleys, mountains, coasts, and cities. On the first journey the older birds guide the young, and the latter never forget what has been taught them. Perhaps birds also plot their course, to some extent, by the sun."

But the Pacific golden plover, which we have named before, travels twenty-five hundred miles over water, without a single sign to guide it. If it were to plot its course by the sun (repeating its calculations every minute, for the position of the sun changes and it carries neither map nor compass) it would have to be exact to the nearest half-degree, for fear of missing its objective, or even failing to catch sight of it altogether. And what is to be said for migrants by night? Are they guided by the stars? All these, except the polestar, move across the sky, and can we expect a bird to distinguish this among the others? It is true that its progress may be slowed down by a cloud which further blackens the night, but this is not an absolute rule. All over the world, thousands and thousands of birds pursue their routes, day and night, even in cloudy weather.

Scientists have given their lives to unraveling this enigma, and their research and observation have led them to this definite conclusion: birds do not need to go over a given itinerary even once in order to pick the right direction and follow it, without error, to the very end. At the bird sanctuary of Rossitten, Professor Thienemann banded young storks, taken from the nest. At the time of the autumnal migration he held them back until the adults had taken flight and flown a considerable distance. As soon as the young storks were freed they set off, unhesitatingly, in the right direction, and were later found in the same wintering places as their parents. A few were delayed along the way, but all these kept to the shortest path toward their goal.

Do birds, then, possess a particular power of orientation, a sort of sixth sense which is denied to man? Here are a few opinions based on the most recent experiments:

"Birds, like compasses, are sensitive to terrestrial magnetism; the semicircular canals of the ear make them sensitive to its currents."

"Carrier pigeons are disturbed in their flight by near-by radio and television stations. They are guided by a system of Hertzian waves whose organization still escapes us."

"Crows and storks, caught in the course of migration and released far from the place of capture, start off along a line *parallel* to the one which they were following. Their ability consists, therefore, not in traveling from one point to another, but rather in moving in a given direction, guided perhaps by their perception of the earth's magnetic currents."

By whom was the direction set or given? And how are we to explain the fact that migratory birds correct the deviations in their course brought about by the wind? Utterly disregarding scientists' experimental interference, they travel in a straight line to their destination, even when they are making the trip for the very first time.

But even the best navigator may encounter an adverse Fate, a combination of elemental forces which it is beyond his powers to overcome.

The wild geese saw the great snowy mountain, outlined against the sky. Over its summit and beyond the eastern ridge, the sky was comparatively clear. But the wide space between the two converging summits was a mass of whistling, white air. Oblique columns of snow dust, some of them two hundred feet high, torn from the mountain sides, whirled through the air, until suddenly they were split in two, toppled over into a horizontal position, where they bounced and then half a second later were swallowed up by the wind. Other columns rose to take their place, merged one with another, whirled about, and then were swallowed up in their turn. Downward flurries of wind ravaged the mountain sides with almost carnivorous ferocity; great layers of snow were raised and torn to bits as if in a pair of invisible jaws. On the west ridge, more fully exposed to the wind, there was a vertical crest of snow, so dense that it seemed as if it must be solid, whereas in reality it was continually destroyed and re-created by the ninety-mile-an-hour gale. The massive immobility of the mountain itself, under this assault, was more impressive than a tempest-torn sea, more disquieting than the fury that raged about it.

This was the sight which greeted the members of the first Everest expedition, in 1921, at the end of the summer monsoon. It was like the landscape of some inhuman planet, a world which had to be of stone in order to resist the onslaught of wind and cold, too suffocating for even the stoutest human frame to bear. As Leigh-Mallory put it: "To see, in fact, was enough. The wind had settled the question; it would have been folly to go on."

It was at this same time of year that a large part of the army of migratory wild geese had to cross the Himalayan chain. At the altitude of this last barrier the atmospheric pressure was less than half of that in which warm-blooded species habitually live, breathe, and have their being. As the tiers of V-formations approached Mount Everest, the squadron of Anser and Anatis was flying at the height of the ridges which converged at the highest peak, with a pyramidal mountain rising independently on the left side.

Instinctively the geese maneuvered to maintain their line of flight against the moving mass of air which pushed them toward the pyramidal mountain. The eddy of whirling white snow seemed to have momentarily slackened, and the army of flying kites continued to move forward, in spite of the sideward pressure. Already the first V's had left the pyramid behind and proudly gained sufficient altitude to pass over the barrier directly before them. Just at this moment an oblique air current came down like a vulture, like a mass of vultures, upon them, raising a cloud of snow from the slopes of the mountain. Instantly there was a hole among the army of geese, as hundreds of them were hurtled against the slopes on their left side. Many of them cut halfway through the snow, like a knifeblade through butter, and were never seen to emerge on the other side. Other tiny gray splotches were crushed on the rocky walls and disappeared no less completely. A few managed to pull away and flutter, like moths, as they were dragged vertically down. Between the mountain walls a disorganized mass of birds struggled against the whirlwinds of snow, pitifully trying to rise above them.

A horizontal ledge, less than ten feet wide, ran obliquely across the west side of the mountain, under a layer of snow considerably diminished by the action of the wind. Now, as often happens in the middle of the day, the wind had abated. All over the surface of the ledge there were holes in the snow, and in these holes were feathery, for the most part inert, gray bodies. A few dying birds continued to stir, beating their wings spasmodically in the snow. Life seemed reluctant to quit them, even at the sub-zero altitude of 23,000 feet. Any human spectator would have wished for a prompt end to their pain.

But perhaps not all the birds were dying. Three or four of them continued to beat their wings, without seeming to give way. Indeed Anser seemed to be recovering his strength. On being thrown against the vertical stone wall he had lost his senses altogether. The birds caught in the oblique air current had been like shooters of precipitous rapids crashing against a rock in the way. After a while, he had begun to struggle, half consciously, against the snow; and when he came to he tried to free himself from it. His head and left wing were painful, but no bones seemed to be broken. Disengaging his breast, he managed to walk through the snow, using his wings like arms to push it back. He waddled upward, leaving a furrow behind him.

After a few yards the ledge narrowed, and a little farther on it broke off. Anser was squeezed in between the vertical wall above and the abyss below. To the right, long lines of flexible, triangular kites flew majestically by. Nothing could stop the geese's migration. The wind was still blowing hard enough to make a take-off from the narrow ledge extremely dangerous, especially because the snow prevented Anser from flapping his wings as usual at the beginning of a flight. At the end of the ledge he turned around and honked, without receiving any answer. There was something pathetic about his unanswered honk in this desolate mountain.

Anser followed his own trail back to the point of departure. He did not linger there, but continued downward, pushing the snow out of his way and still honking. The effort to advance through the snow must have been exhausting, for from time to time his honking stopped, like the call of a man who is being gradually asphyxiated.

A few yards farther down, the ledge narrowed and merged with the wall. Just before this point, there was a right-angle turn, which gave shelter to a sort of platform running from northwest to southeast. This longish platform was composed of slanting rocky slabs, overlaid like shingles and extremely slippery, although they were not actually covered with snow. Here Anser shook his wings. He could probably have taken off. Instead he walked up and down, shaking his wings and honking. When finally another call answered his, he returned resolutely to the ledge and pushed his way, like a plow through the snow. His honking had by now roused two different responses, but Anser did not pause or change direction. He had recognized the voice of Anatis, and it was to her that he was so stubbornly fraying a path.

Finally he made out his mate's head and neck and rubbed his own, several times, against them. The two birds gabbled together and wheeled around in the snow. Then Anser started back along the furrow which he had just made. Anatis followed after. Two other survivors were struggling through the snow in the same direction. They too were fighting for their lives on this narrow ledge 23,000 feet above sea level. Anatis, after getting out of her hole, proceeded very slowly, making frequent stops to look back and honk. But there was no answer. Behind the four survivors there was only a row of dead bodies. The goslings, whom Anatis was calling, must either have been thrown into a fatal collision with the mountain or else have perished in the holes in the snow. Meanwhile the other two survivors had pushed on ahead of Anser. Soon they reached the platform and shook the snow from their wings.

Anser paused to call Anatis, who was still calling her brood. The few yards which they had still to travel along the ledge seemed interminable. There came a moment when Anser saw the other couple take the air. In the shelter provided by the right-angle turn of the wall, they took several steps forward, flapping their wings, and then left the ground. They rose parallel to the mountain side, described a semicircle, two-thirds of a circle, then before an air current could deflect them too far, they began to row with all their strength in a southerly direction. Although they were still far below the main body of the army of geese, Everest-bound, they gradually gained altitude; and it was clear that eventually they would rejoin the great migratory army.

Anatis had finally reached the platform, and now she followed the example of Anser in shaking the snow from her wings. But her movements were not normal, for she flapped her wings no more than two or three times. Anser walked nervously up and down, sliding on the slippery rock and honking at her impatiently. Probably he had not noticed that a large segment of her left wing hung down, like the end of a half-broken branch. Indeed, Anatis had fractured this wing. She stood at the edge of the platform, still honking in the direction of the snowy ledge. Anser came back and walked around her, making a cooing sound. At last she must have given up the idea of finding her goslings for she followed him onto the slabs of bare, slippery stone.

Anser took a few steps forward, flapping his wings, and rose into the air. He rose parallel to the mountain side and described a semicircle. But Anatis did not follow. She stepped forward, sliding on the slippery rock, and flapped her wings, without being able to leave the ground. There she stood, on the platform, with her left wing half open and hanging down. Anser was already far away. The air current had momentarily deflected him, but then he gained altitude and began to row with powerful strokes through the sky. Already he was no more than a tiny, gray-winged body in the immense sea of air over the mountains. Anatis turned her head to one side and looked at him, without moving.

Anser came back. Anatis saw him looming, larger and larger, until finally he began to combat the near-by air current and maneuver for a landing. When he came within the area protected by the mountain wall he glided down, thrusting out his legs and bringing himself onto the platform. Here he honked and gabbled as loudly as he could, calling Anatis, moving so close that he could touch her chest with his and then walking away. Anatis followed him the length of the platform, occasionally flapping her wings before she came to a stop. Apparently Anser did not understand.

Perhaps he did understand; perhaps he saw the fractured wing. But the migratory impulse exercised a tyrannical power over every cell in his body. Anatis, too, must have felt the same impulse, for she stepped forward again on the slippery slabs and tried to flap her wings. A dozen times she tried vainly to follow Anser's example, while he flew in circles near by and then came back to the ground. The repeated take-offs from the slippery rock surface must have been exhausting, but he continued to make them. The migratory impulse had to be obeyed. Yet, at the same time, it was clear that he could not make up his mind to leave Anatis alone; the bond of affection between them was too strong. He was a pathetic sight, torn between these two forces and certainly suffering something like mental pain, as was evident from the despairing outcry which he made every time he alighted on the rocks and tried to induce Anatis to follow him. As time went by, it seemed as if he would continue his unsuccessful attempts forever.

Some fifty times Anatis had tried to take off, but now she gave up trying. She followed Anser a short distance across the slabs, sliding one way and another, but when he made as if to take flight she stopped in her tracks and sought the shelter of the overhanging wall. Unless Anser were to be completely exhausted, it looked as if he might kill his mate by subjecting her to such strain. Meanwhile, over the mountains, the army of geese continued to fly interminably by.

The sky had turned gray. To the west, above the curved summit of Mount Everest, there was a gleam from the setting sun. The wind died away, but the layer of snow on the ledge gradually hardened, so that every dead bird lay in a frozen nest. The temperature must have dropped to at least 20 degrees below zero. Anatis was crouching motionless, in one corner of the rocky platform, close to the vertical wall. And Anser crouched, just as motionless, beside her. The combat between the two warring forces was over, and affection had won. At least, that was how it seemed.

When Anser first saw Anatis seek refuge against the wall, he ceased taking off into the air but continued to pace up and down the platform, calling to her, walking first toward her and then away. Then, at long last, he gave up. He went over to Anatis and crouched beside her, so close that their bodies touched. No doubt he was thoroughly exhausted and thought he would rest for a few hours before renewing his efforts. Perhaps that was it. The instinct of self-preservation must have warned him that it was madness to stay still in the cold air of the mountain heights, which was bound to chill still further as the night went on. Yet Anser crouched beside Anatis and did not stir. Never since the far-away summer when they had pledged their troth to each other in the Ganges valley, had he been without her. She was a part of himself and he could not possibly leave her behind. Neither the instinct of self-preservation nor the tyrannical migratory impulse could bring him to do so.

The inseparably faithful couple crouched against the wall, their heads tucked under their wings and their bodies warming each other. But the heat of their bodies waned from one minute to the next, and the hour was coming when it would be altogether gone. Life abandoned the two bodies, pressed together forever on the icy mountain side, at almost the very same time. In the immense space of the twilight sky tiers of wild geese continued to fly. The flexible, triangular kites winged their way toward the south, toward the sunny place of hibernation, where the life of the species was to be perpetuated.

CHAPTER II

NAVIGATORS WITHOUT A COMPASS

1

The shadow of the conical, rocky mountain was projected with a clarity unbearable to the human eye upon the rocky plain. Sun and stars were shining together in the dark sky; the temperature was near 180 degrees, but it would sink to 240 below zero by the time the dead sphere accomplished half of its incredibly slow rotation. Day or night, in boiling heat or interplanetary cold, the same, dark, atmosphereless sky hung over the brown, rocky mountains and the plain, studded with craters, below. And in the sky hung the planet Earth, seen now as a disk, now as an almost disappearing crescent, with its continents marked by dark splotches.

The Moon progressed in its orbit at the speed of thirty miles a minute, the image of stillness, silence, and sterility. No matter how hard the life-giving flames of the sun beat against this rocky surface, there was no hope of a responsive growth of any kind. The clear-cut shadows of the mountains moved slowly over the rocky plain, and that was all. The infinite movement of the universe came here to a dead end, symbolized by the shape of the craters, a zero.

No! Two hundred fifty thousand miles away, billions of molecules of salt water were displaced by the dead sphere's gravitation. The great mass of all the Earth's oceans rose and fell in exact time with the displacement of the shadow cast by the rocky mountains of the Moon. And this motion of the tide was followed by billions of living creatures.

The slim silvery bodies of the grunions gleamed on the crest of the waves beating upon the California shore. Each one of these tiny fish, male or female, was swollen with milky seminal fluid or eggs, ready for fertilization. Every year, during the three nights after the full moon between May and June, these silversides arrive from the deep sea. They have set out in time to arrive on these exact nights and no others, for the job they have to do admits of neither advance nor delay.

The tide was rising. The gleaming grunions sported in the waves, letting themselves be carried nearly to the beach before they flicked their tails and turned back. For the hour had not yet come. The tide was almost at flood, but the grunions were waiting for it to turn, for the exact moment when it would start to ebb. They had calculated this moment more accurately than either man or his machines.

"Here is our robot tide predictor," said the government engineer to the newspaper reporter. "With it we can calculate the time and height of the tide for any day, past, present, or future. In any given place the time varies from day to day, because it depends on the rotation of the earth and the respective positions of Earth, Moon and Sun, which are never exactly the same. We have to feed the electronic robot not only equations expressing astronomical movements and their mechanical consequences on the mass of the water, but also a coefficient peculiar to the locality, which is called the 'establishment of the past.' This, once calculated, accounts for all the local factors, such as the configuration of the coast, which affect the planetary phenomena. Moreover we must, at times, modify the equations fed to the robot, making allowance for a number of astronomical inequalities which it has been necessary to treat as negligible or else constant, in order to avoid positively monstrous computations. The approximate figures which we finally obtain vary by two to six inches from the actual height of the tides and by a matter of minutes from their time."

On the California beach the waves followed one after another, lapping repeatedly over the same area of sand, without passing the high-water mark. Two hundred fifty thousand miles away the shadows of the rocky, brown mountains moved slowly across the plains of the moon. Suddenly a wave broke and stopped a few inches short of the line attained by its predecessor, and then a a second and then a third. The tide had turned, and the grunions, which so far had stuck to the crests of the waves, let themselves be rolled onto the sand. Each couple accomplished the transmission of life in the short space of time between one wave and another: the female laid her eggs on the wet sand and the male fertilized them. The wave after the one which had carried both fish in carried them both away.

In order to hatch, the eggs had to remain two weeks in the warm, damp sand. There they stayed. There was no danger of their being swept away by the waves the night when they were laid, because it was exactly then that the tide started to ebb. And the following nights would be equally safe, because the amplitude of the tide was scheduled to diminish. Two weeks later, with the advent of the new moon, the tide would have the same sweep as upon the night of the spawning; it would free the matured eggs from the sand, and as the young fish emerged they would put out at once to sea. The operation was carried out with clocklike, or rather with astronomical, precision. If the grunions, like the tide predictor, ever had made an error of only a few minutes, the eggs would never have matured and the whole species would long since have become extinct. Of course, this fish is not a wizard at calculation. It lives and swims in the sea and is an integral part of it. Its activity is tuned to the rhythm of the sea, that is, to the movement of the stars.

As a child I passed a number of summer holidays near Roscoff, on the north coast of Brittany. Needless to say, I took particular delight in hunting and fishing at low tide, in the discovery of shrimp and plaice left by the ebb tide in pools along the beach, of the crabs asleep under a layer of seaweed, who stuck out their claws when I overturned the rock under which they had found protection, of the bright "eyes" of clams half hidden by the wet, marvelously smooth sand. Here and there, between the high- and low-water marks I also saw great green patches, but without wondering what they might be. Before the tide returned, flooding the domain of my exploration, the patches disappeared. . . .

These patches came at once before my mind's eye when I read Rachel Carson's admirable book, *The Sea Around Us*. There I found the explanation of a phenomenon which I had to a large extent forgotten.

A little sea worm, known as *Convoluta roscoffensis* from the place where it has been most often observed, feeds exclusively on a certain type of green seaweed. For assimilating this it needs the light of the sun; and that is why, when the tide ebbs, it exposes itself to the sun for several hours, while the seaweed is changed into starch and sugar, which pass directly into its body. When the process of digestion is over and the tide is coming in, Convoluta burrows into the sand, in order not to be carried out into deep water. And so it continues, rhythmically, to come to the surface with the ebb tide and take cover with the flood, appearing and disappearing in green patches.

Scientists have gathered colonies of these worms and placed them in tanks on beds of sand soaked with salt water. And they have found that twice a day the worms come to the surface of the sand and then burrow under it, exactly as if they were on the beach. Far from the sea, surrounded by the white walls of a laboratory, *Convoluta roscoffensis* still heeds the rhythm of the tides.

How curious that in the midst of the oceans living creatures should show their dependence on the cosmos so strikingly! On land or in the air they seem to behave, whether alone or in groups, far more independently. Actually all of them, including man, depend more or less directly on the movement of the stars, which causes changes of climate and determines the growth of vegetation. But while the visible crust of the Earth seems to be solid and free, or at least not continuously subject to the forces of gravitation, every particle of the liquid mass which submerges three-quarters of its total area responds continuously to the call of the heavens.

The amplitude of the tides which raise and lower this liquid mass varies in accordance with cycles determined by the motion of heavenly bodies hundreds of thousands or millions of miles away. (The distance of the sun, which exercises an influence half as powerful as that of the moon, is, we may remember, 93,000,000 miles.) This same motion, or displacement, together with thermal variations creates and maintains the dominant "planetary winds" which the unceasing rotation of the Earth deflects. From the equator to the poles, there is a constant circulatory movement of cold and warm water, sparked by a great pulsation whose periods occur in extremely complicated cycles, also determined by the relative positions of Earth, Moon, and Sun. These layers of warm and cold water rise to the surface and fall, top and replace one another, create areas of greater or lesser salinity, and it is in their shifting reflection of the starry universe that the creatures of the sea move and have their being.

December. Gusts of icy wind blow over the English Channel. Herring swim at a dizzy speed through the cold water. Each silvery, hydrodynamic body, propelled by a miraculous caudal fin, moves effortlessly through the surrounding fluid, and all of them together, like thousands of arrows shot from the same bow, move in a single direction. Suddenly, without slackening speed, the whole shoal makes a sharp turn, more expertly than any squad of drilling soldiers could ever achieve it.

For weeks and months the herring have swum in scattered groups over a wide area of water, looking for food, and devouring tiny, deep-sea shellfish, or whole shoals of sprats and other such miniatures on their way. Off the Scandinavian coast thousands upon thousands of them, engaged in this same voracious pursuit, have thrown themselves into the dragnets. But such numbers are quite insignificant. From the northern seas there have been reports of herring shoals over ninety miles long and numbering as many as a hundred billion fish.

At the time we have described the herring have no thought of hunting. They are swimming in closer formation, the females heavy with hundreds of thousands of eggs and the males with the seed to fertilize them. The all-powerful call to perpetuate the species has sounded.

Most fish reproduce by external fecundation. And yet, by

some apparent carelessness on the part of Nature, the male sperm perishes only a few seconds after contact with water. The impregnation of the eggs must take place almost instantaneously. Certain coastal and river fish, like birds, protect the fertilized eggs by placing them in nests. Using grass stuck together with a secretion from his own kidneys, the male stickleback constructs a sleeve-shaped nest and invites the passing females to enter. As soon as one has been persuaded to go in and lay her eggs, he does his part and then installs himself in the nest and makes the fanning movement necessary to bring about oxygenation. The fighting fish of the mildly saline waters around Indochina rises to the surface of the water in order to inhale air which it breathes out almost immediately in tiny balls covered with mucus, to be made into a sort of transparent raft-shaped nest for its young. The labrus lines a rocky cave with seaweed. Certain catfish protect the fertilized eggs by holding them in their mouths, but at times are induced by hunger to swallow them. Among sea horses, the male tucks them into an abdominal pocket, like that of the kangaroo. His courtship includes a preliminary parade or display of an extremely graceful and complicated kind. And as for herring . . .

The spawning ground is an area of cold sea, where the fish gather in a teeming, hysterical mass, pushing one against another. While they are in this state of hyperexcitement, first the females and then the males effect their ejections, and life is transmitted. There is no question of a nest or anything remotely resembling it. The fecundated eggs are immediately forgotten and abandoned. Billions of them are lost, devoured by other fish as are also billions of the surviving young, which never attain maturity. What does it matter? Here Nature throws life away with mad prodigality and fulfills its designs by sheer weight of numbers. Fortunately for man, the herring and many other fish which reproduce in the same way continue to abound in the sea.

"It is a serious mistake to imagine that bread and beefsteaks are man's chief sources of nutrition," I was recently told by Professor Budker, a member of various international groups concerned with the exploration of the sea. "The greater part of mankind lives off rice and dried fish."

This fact is quite obvious, particularly if one looks with proper perspective at the human situation, if one remembers that China contains one-fourth the population of the globe, and that the Japanese alone take five million tons of fish out of the sea every year. But let us not linger too long in Asia.

For centuries the herring (my readers will soon see that there is a definite reason for my choice of this fish) has been an essential factor in the nutrition of Europe. During the Middle Ages it was hawked about every town; the herring catch, transportation, and sale combined to form one of the greatest single sectors of trade, and military leaders made salted herring into a basic military ration. Later on, salted cod and refrigerated fresh fish reduced the sway of his majesty King Herring. Nevertheless, a million tons—two billion pounds—are still caught and eaten in Europe every year. Every year the herring season opens in May, June, and July, off Norway, the Shetlands and Orkneys, and extends gradually to the south. In August herring are caught off Scotland; in September, off Denmark and England; in October, along the banks of Flanders. The fishermen of Dieppe and Fécamp put out to sea in November and December, and the Bretons in January. After that, there are no more herring to be found, until they turn up again in the north the following year. For a long time this phenomenon was explained as follows:

"Herring prefer fairly cold water, between 40 and 60 degrees. During the summer they linger, and eat abundantly, in the northern seas; with the approach of autumn, in order not to undergo a change of temperature, they move south. Then, in the dead of winter, they go deep down, seeking relief from the cold, and make their way gradually north, where we find them again at the beginning of summer."

This was a clear enough program of migration. But one day some scientists who had never stirred from their laboratories began to dispute it.

"Herring don't travel, or at least not outside a very limited radius. We know, because we've counted their vertebrae."

"And what have vertebrae to do with it?"

"They've taught us that there are not merely herring, but herring of many kinds, which the number of vertebrae permit us to identify. From birth to death the number of a herring's vertebrae is invariable; but in samples caught in various places this number is not the same. There are an Icelandic herring, a Norwegian herring, a Norfolk herring, a Dutch herring, and many more. The number of vertebrae decreases with the salinity of the water. Each herring is adapted to its own surroundings and can live in no other."

"Then how do you explain the shifting field of fishing operations?"

A few minutes is enough to make this quite understandable. Imagine a great invisible heart, below the equator, not far under the surface of the sea. This heart beats very slowly, in fact, only once a year. Every spring it contracts, giving a horizontal push to a superficial mass of highly saline, warm, tropical water, which travels up the Atlantic in a northeasterly direction, to the Bay of Biscay, the English Channel, the Irish Sea, the North Sea and the coasts of Ireland and Norway. In the autumn this heart dilates, and the warm water returns, retreating before a mass of cold water from the pole.

Cold water, as we have seen, is what herring prefer. And so when the warm-water ceiling advances northward from the equator, the herring plunge deeper. That is why, at this time, they are no longer to be found near the surface. At the end of summer, when the warm-water ceiling retreats, the herrings return to their former level. The return to the surface is made on a staggered timetable, from north to south, giving the impression of a vast horizontal movement, when it is in reality a vertical or, to be exact, an oblique one. We have already seen that the different varieties of herring move horizontally as well, but only to a limited extent. Nature's movements are exempt from rigidity.

A French scientist, Le Danois, was the first to define the pulsating marine heart of which we have just spoken and to apply the terms "transgressive" and "regressive" to the masses of equatorial and polar water. Their displacement explains the migration of the seasonal fish which supply man with so much of his food and allow him to clock its time. The cod, which has even less liking than the herring for warm water, moves in the same way, off the coasts of Greenland, Newfoundland, Scotland and in the North Sea. The mackerel, the sardine, and other fish, on the contrary, flee the cold, and manage to stay on the edge of the regressive water, descending and rising again in the same oblique manner. The tuna travels horizontally with the warm current from the tropics all the way to Iceland and beyond, and then flees southward before the cold.

Formerly men were satisfied to be on the watch for the seasonal arrivals of the fish; now they study their migratory movements in order to cast nets and lines with scientific precision. By 1980 the population of the world will be four billion; and the tillable land surface, destroyed over great areas through deforestation or intensive farming, continues to diminish. The human race must either find food in the sea or perish. In an especially equipped research laboratory in Canada, scientists are working to make seaweed acceptable to our palate. This is a praiseworthy effort; but it is doubtful how much pleasure such artificial nourishment can give, whereas fish have a definitely enjoyable flavor and for thousands of years have proved to be health-giving.

Some fish travel obliquely or horizontally through the sea, with the minimum change of environment. Others swim indifferently through warm and cold waters in pursuit of moving plant life or prey. I have written in earlier books about whales and sperm whales, those marine mammals which circle the globe in search of squid or floating masses of plankton, and about seals, amphibious mammals which reproduce on land and then set out to feed in oceans thousands of miles away. All the creatures which draw their food from the sea are affected directly or indirectly by the periodic movements of great masses of water.

Even the areas of migration are not unchanging. Some varieties of cod never seen near Greenland before 1930 are now caught there every year. Cold-water fish seem to be shifting their habitat toward the north. The shifts are due to the gradual increase of global heat, to which other phenomena bear witness as well. On land, vegetation and also a number of animal species are advancing toward the pole; and the average temperature of the waters of the Atlantic has risen. It has been ascertained by precise measurements that this rise is caused by the melting of the northern icecap. And the melting is not the result of mere chance.

I have already spoken, in connection with the herring, of a great, invisible heart, below the equator. Its beat affects only a relatively thin layer of water just under the surface of the sea. But there are other pulsations, produced in the same way by the gravitation of the stars, which take place deeper down and have more far-reaching consequences. The tidal movements of which they are the cause are greatest at the winter solstice when Moon and Sun are so placed as to exercise the maximum of attraction upon the sea. This occurs once in every eighteen centuries. Every time that the deep-lying tropical waters arrive within a certain distance of the pole, the ice starts melting, and a whole cycle of climatic change begins. This now generally admitted theory was first set forth by the Danish oceanographer Petterson, who died in 1941. The Vikings' voyages of exploration took place in areas which ice floes later closed to navigation. The water and the climate of our part of the globe began to cool off around the sixth century; now they are once more in the process of heating.

This cyclical phenomenon may eventually have radical consequences. Today oceanographers are trying to calculate how far the Atlantic Ocean will rise if nothing interrupts its increase of temperature. The whole of the Netherlands and big cities such as London and New York may be threatened with engulfment. . . . If we seem to have come a long way from the subject of fish migration, I have only wished to call attention to the fact that man, proud as he may be of his conquest of nature, is still subject to the great movements of the waters periodically produced by the gravitational power of the stars

2

Certain young things seem from the start to hold high promise. When Salar, the salmon, was only six months old, it was easy to see that he had character. Most assuredly, he was not one of those fish that swim lazily up and down a river, waiting for a square meal to drift by before they make the effort to open their mouths, or that lie low, near the bottom, for hours at a time, barely flicking their tails with a bored air. A sporting fellow, that is what he already gave the impression of being, with a nervous system keyed to movement and adventure. There among his contemporaries, none of them as much as three inches long, he swam vigorously, bucking the current with a rapid, decisive thrust of his small body, as he went after his prey. He was intelligent, too, in his determination. Summer was in full swing in the Massif Central, and the sun which shone on its green slopes cast over the stream the shadow of everything moving on its steep bank. Whenever this happened Salar and his companions darted under pebbles. Suddenly the water seemed as empty as it was clear, and yet a moment later the agile troop was once more breasting the current. Yes, Salar promised to turn out well. But perhaps we should go back and say a word about his birth and antecedents.

His father and mother had come to this part of the stream in the preceding December, at which time they weighed eighteen and twenty-two pounds respectively. All around, the country was bare, and covered with snow. It had taken the two big salmon a whole year to travel up from the sea, fighting frothy rapids, surmounting dams, and resisting fishermen's bait. Turning from one tributary into another, they had come at last to a rippling, three-foot-deep brook that they recognized as their goal, the place where they themselves had been born five years before.

Several other salmon, male and female, arrived at the same time. Salar's mother was carrying something like 30,000 eggs in her bloated abdomen. As soon as she recognized the fine pebbles of the spawning ground, she proceeded to swim over and over the spot, scraping and furrowing it with her belly, while the male followed, in increasing excitement, swerving from time to time to chase away any other males who had the impulse to approach his mate. The speed of the to-and-fro motion grew more intense; the coppery, spindle-shaped fish twisted feverishly in their course. The female contracted and relaxed her abdominal muscles and rubbed her belly against the pebbles until at last the eggs broke out and away. Having eliminated all possible rivals, the male at once ejected his milt.

The amber, spherical eggs, each one about as large as a pea and heavier than water, fell straight to the bottom. Even if you had known where to find them their transparency would probably have made them invisible. No mucus glued them to the pebbles; only their own weight prevented them from being carried away. Inside one of these eggs, as an imperceptible embryo, Salar already had an existence of his own. Through the slender membrane, he absorbed by osmosis the oxygen of the surrounding water, and his nourishment came from the vitelline substance of the egg.

Gradually he took shape, and two tiny black spots marked the emplacement of the eyes. By the beginning of March his growth had freed him from the curling position of an embryo. But he was still less than an inch long, extremely frail, almost transparent, and incapable of moving. Only the incomplete sketch of a fish, he lay motionless at the bottom of the stream, feeding on the yolk sac which hung from his belly.

Toward the end of April this source of supply was exhausted, and he had to look for another. Nature's law demanded that, in these surroundings, he should become a hunter of tiny insects and bugs. Real life had begun, while it was still difficult for him to survive. The inch-long hunter was himself a highly vulnerable prey, and great numbers of his companions must have ended their lives at this time in some larger fish's stomach. Salar was lucky. His translucent body had gathered substance and length: one and a half, two, two and a half inches, he was now golden-brown in color, with darker shading on the back and sides. Although he was still slender, he had acquired courage, intelligence, and agility: he could shoot like an arrow through the water.

With these qualities, Salar was not likely to vegetate. He led a healthy and agreeable life, devoted largely to the hunt, gaining constantly in weight, length, and vigor. At eighteen months he was six inches long, and his coloring would have rejoiced a painter's eye: his back was dark olive-green with bronze reflections; his belly and sides, paler with eight or ten vertical stripes the same color as his back, and studded with red and black dots. A salmon of this age is called a "parr."

Salar seemed happy enough in his native stream. He lived peaceably, or at least exempt from overt war, with the trout, bullheads, lampreys, and loaches, which peopled its waters. But during the second winter after his parents had laid him, in the form of a transparent pea, on the stream bed, his manner suddenly changed. Until then the young parr had lived, like his brothers and sisters, near the original spawning ground, in close company, to be sure, but swimming each one on his own, quite independently of the rest. Now, little by little, without realizing it, they fell into closer ranks, into groups and shoals, which dived and maneuvered all together, like herring, with their movement transmitted from one to another, as if in waves. At the same time their coats changed color and became still more beautiful: their backs were steel-blue, their sides white, flecked with silver. Every shoal streaked through the water like a flight of shining arrows. Under this new guise, the lordly salmon is known as a "smolt."

Melting snow and spring rains had swollen the brook to the point of overflowing. None of the smolts lingered near the bottom; they all stayed in the central current, with their heads pointing upstream. From time to time they bucked the current and threw themselves, all together, upon some prey; then, all together, they retreated to their original immobile position. Their heads still pointed upstream, but the current carried them down. The spawning ground was far distant now; both banks and the bed of the river fell away. But the smolts made no effort to oppose the current; they were content to stay in the center of it and let it pull them backward. When night came, they continued to drift in the same way. The descent to the sea had begun.

It was a strange journey. With the light of day the smolts seemed to be galvanized into action. They swam against the current, hunted in shoals, more energetically than ever before keeping to the middle of the stream, masters of the current. Then, when night fell, they resumed their positions on their watery couch and let themselves be carried along.

The brook flowed into another, and this into a river. Occasionally there was a dam in the way, and the whole shoal spilled over it into the foaming waters below. To the rippling mountain streams succeeded the placid flow of a mighty river, yellow with alluvial mud and growing gradually salty. The journey had extended through days into weeks when the smolts drew near the sea.

Most fresh-water fish cannot endure being plunged for more than a few seconds into salt water, and many salt-water fish are susceptible to the least change of salinity; we have seen how they migrate in order to keep the same surroundings. But the smolts, born and grown in the fresh, highly oxygenated waters of a mountain stream, showed no uneasiness when they entered the brackish waters near the estuary.

The tide rose, and the sea mingled its waters with those of the river. Salar swam without effort, letting this slow movement carry him along. When the tide ebbed, he went out with it, to the coast. For several successive tides he remained in the estuary, alternately attracted and repelled by the sea. Night came, and he did not see the beams of the lighthouse; and when day followed he did not leap out of the waves to discover the immense horizon which had replaced the near banks of his native stream. Even if he had had such curiosity, his eyes, adapted for under-water use, would not have served him. But his highly developed chemical perception told him that he had left his childhood domain, and that a whole new realm extended before and around him. The water was not the same, and the prey had a different and more intense taste. This was the sea, the true home of adventurers.

With every ebb tide, the young salmon swam farther away from the coast. It was far out in the salty sea that he felt he could find his adult food, develop his full strength, and become a magnificent and intrepid lord, like his father. He disported himself with increasing ease, farther and farther from the shore, and after several days he steered resolutely outward, leaving the fresh inland streams and the friendly coast behind him. Down below the rolling green waves, he swam powerfully toward the high sea.

An object less than nine inches long and only a pound in weight is hardly more than a speck in the sea. But let us momentarily drop Salar and his companions. Two, three, four, or five years later the fish swimming through the estuary in the opposite direction will be twenty to forty inches in length and weigh between nine and thirty-three pounds. And these full-grown salmon will be our same smolts—of that we can be quite sure. Many of them were marked on their way down to the sea, in order to make them recognizable upon their return, and an examination of their scales will permit us to figure out their exact age.

The migration of the salmon is singularly beautiful to observe, and its motives are strikingly enigmatic. Born in an inland stream, they attain nearly two years of age before going down to the sea. Later they return unfailingly to the same river mouth, swim upstream, and pass from tributary to tributary until at last they arrive at the spawning ground where they came into existence. The proved ability to make this unfailing return is stupefying. How in the world do they do it?

Scientists found this question a poser, or proffered thoroughly untenable theories until it occurred to them to replace the "how" with "why." Even after this, they continued to grope in the dark until only four or five years ago a French observer, Maurice Fontaine, pointed out the following solution:

"The sea-bound smolts are the ones to study. Our first query should be: Why do the smolts quit their native stream?"

Why, indeed? The young salmon's urge to go down to

the sea seems at first to be natural enough—like an adolescent's desire to set sail and tour the globe—and yet it is really quite unreasonable. An animal which has grown and prospered in certain surroundings should not wish to abandon them. There is no romantic literature to tell him: "Somewhere else you'll be far more happy!" And fish of other kinds, born and grown beside him, do not feel the same impulse. Is it all a matter of heredity? His parents, in their time, were just as happy upstream. And so, what? I wish to steer clear of technicalities, to avoid anything that might distract the reader from the spectacle with which I hope to entertain him. But there are certain things which we cannot even notice unless we are prepared to understand them.

"The young salmon's wanderlust comes upon him just when his coat changes color. As a parr his pigmentation has protected him from the light, but as a silvery smolt he feels bare and searches for darker waters. As he passes down a succession of rivers in which he can swim progressively deeper, he comes at last to the sea."

This is a simple rendering of an explanation which won acceptance for some time. As the scientists put it: "Negative phototropism urges the smolt down to the sea." Of course a tropism is an attraction. But other scientists refuted this idea, stating:

"Tropisms don't take us very far. They explain nothing more than instinct—a word which has long since been banished from the scientific vocabulary. If we are to throw negative phototropism at our young salmon, we must be able to trace a continuous progression toward increasing darkness. And he makes no such progression at all. Then there is another disquieting factor: certain young salmon do not migrate with their brothers when they are two years old. They attain sexual maturity in their native stream and sometimes fecundate the eggs of the full-grown females which have come back from the sea. We must look farther for an explanation."

I have mentioned Maurice Fontaine. It is difficult to summarize in a few lines the results of several years of painstaking research, but his conclusion may be briefly stated as follows: the salmon's migratory urge is due to variations in intensity of the functioning of certain glands.

The silvery hue taken on by the smolt is not a matter of sheer chance; it is a manifestation of hyperthyroid activity. Without entering into the details of glandular interaction, we may say that the modification of neuroendocrine activity which accompanies the young parr's development into a smolt is closely related to the impulse to start down to the sea. In fact, migrants differ from nonmigrants by virtue of the greater fluctuations in their cycle of neuroendocrine activity. When these fluctuations attain a certain level, there is a break in the equilibrium between the fish's organism and its surroundings, or, if you like, an increase of the organism's sensitivity to meteorological variations. The smolt is in a hypersensitive and unstable condition, and the first spring flood releases the migratory impulse. Its physical disposition being favorable, the slightest external event is "like the spark which sets off the powder-train." This seems to me quite clear, or at least intuitively comprehensible. Without falling into any anthropomorphic fallacy, we cannot but be reminded of certain changes in our own behavior which present-day science attributes, beyond doubt or discussion, to our glands.

And what happens to the salmon when they reach the sea? They simple disappear. Ten years ago no salmon had ever been caught by deep-sea fishermen.

"They go far out," said the proponents of negative photo-tropism, "and stay deep down. The salmon is a fish of the ocean depths although, paradoxically enough, another tropism calls it back to the spawning ground in the river."

"They don't go far out, they simply dive deep," said advocates of a rival theory. "They never leave the continental shelf, but linger in former river estuaries, now submerged. No wonder it is so easy for them to find their way back up the river they came down; they have never left it."

But between February and June of 1948, some mackerel fishers from Douarnenez caught a hundred and thirty full-grown salmon, weighing an average of eleven pounds. Their fishing-ground lay a hundred miles west of Land's End, the tip of Cornwall, and they were using surface nets, which were nowhere submerged farther than ten feet. In the years that followed, many smolts which had been marked in the river were caught six hundred to twelve hundred miles from the coast. Some of these were marked a second time, thrown back into the water, and then caught for a third time near their original spawning ground, in the stream.

Yes, the salmon swims out to the high sea. This lordly fish, this shining samurai, does not waste his time, like a poltroon, in some shallow estuary. And out in the stormy deep he does not skulk near the bottom, like a beetle, fearful of the light of day. He does probably dive far, but then he comes up again to swim and hunt at the surface, feeling perfectly at home in any part of this element. And why should he not be increasingly happy? His strength and speed are such that he can either instigate an attack or elude a pursuer. If within the space of four or five years he increases in weight from one to as much as thirty-three pounds, it is obvious that he has not been leading a fearful, second-rate existence. And yet when he has reached the pink of physical perfection and sexual maturity, another irresistible urge impels him to leave his happy hunting-grounds in the sea and return to the fresh water of an inland stream. Why?

"Just because he has attained sexual maturity. Nature's first law demands that he transmit the life of his kind. The first step is to transform his bodily reserves into reproductive elements, and along with this goes a phenomenon of oxidation. The salmon needs more oxygen, and in search of it he is impelled to return first to the coast and then up the more and more highly oxygenated rivers. Positive branchiotropism—there's the source not only of the salmon's urge but also of his sense of direction. His chemical sensitivity is so highly developed that on his way up from the coast he rediscovers the part of the stream where the oxygen content of the water is exactly the same as that to which he was accustomed in his childhood."

Another tropism, is that it? This time the picture is crystal-clear and very attractive. For a long time, indeed, it held the theorists' attention. Only a few years ago, an English study of the salmon spoke with complete assurance of the search for oxygen as the propulsive power. But the theory of branchiotropism crumbled, at least with regard to salmon, when Claude Francis-Bœuf, a French scientist, proved that estuaries contain less oxygen than either a river or—the sea. It is too much to believe that a salmon coming from the sea will aim at a less oxygenated zone because he knows that there is an abundance of oxygen beyond it!

Then is the origin of the impulse a sexual one? Observation showed that when the salmon started back toward the coast their sexual glands were in repose; it was only later that they entered into activity. Once more, there seemed to be no explanation. Here again, if we go back to the theory of Maurice Fontaine, things become if not crystal-clear, at least to a large degree explicable. Both phenomena—the silvery coat which marks the transformation of the parr into a smolt and the extraordinary growth attained by the salmon in the deep sea—point to intense thyroid activity. It is, then, under the impulsion of the thyroid—"that little interior demon," as Professor Budker described it to me—that the salmon decides to leave first his native stream and then the deep sea. In both cases, it is a matter of *going somewhere*. But let us be more definite: the thyroid creates a condition favorable to departure.

In the second case, the return to the river, what external event triggers the migratory mechanism? We have not the slightest idea. Are there definite routes and points of departure, at which the salmon assemble? The points at which salmon have been caught dot the map off Brittany, Cornwall, Scotland, Norway, and northern Russia. The only certainty has already been set forth here: salmon do swim out into the sea, and from it they return.

How do they guide themselves on the return voyage? The answer is marvelous, but we do not know it. At the very moment when the raised curtain might open up the most amazing perspective on the migrant's sense of direction and disclose hitherto unknown relationships between living organisms and the universe, secret truths capable of overturning the whole structure of human knowledge—at this magic instant we are forced to say: "No, the curtain is not raised, not yet."

From a distant stretch of sea, perhaps of a considerable area, where Salar has lived and swum over a period of several years, he now sets his course for the shore. Not for any unspecified place on the shore, but for the river mouth from which he has come. Without benefit of sun or stars or compass, without error or hesitation, as is proved by his speed of sixty miles a day, he travels through a liquid element in which no signpost is to be found until he reaches the estuary.

But the most dramatic part of the journey is still ahead. There is no need to plot the scenes in such a way as to bring in a sequence of external events, real or imagined. The salmon's fate is played out within himself.

Salar felt the estuary around him. From the very beginning of the return journey he had known where it was and steered unhesitatingly toward it; but now he definitely felt it. The water of a river remains somewhat fresh a considerable distance out to sea, and Salar's chemical sensitivity was more acute than that of any mechanical apparatus for measuring saline content. He swam very fast, faster than when he had left the coast or even when he had chased his prey far out at sea. Three feet long now and weighing twenty-two pounds, truly he was a superb sight, with his steel-blue back and his pink belly sprinkled with spots of bright red. Many a fisherman would have been proud to be photographed beside him! Little did Salar know that pitiless Nature would demand the sacrifice of this beauty.

Salar passed the estuary and entered the river. The spawning ground was five hundred miles away; in the interior, ponds were frozen over and there was an icy crust here and there along the banks of the river. Together with several other big salmon, Salar was swimming up the Loire. As he passed under its bridges, his swift, rocketlike body may have caught the eye of some casual beholder; but there are few pedestrians or fishermen in such places on a winter day when the wind is blowing or a cold rain is falling, and before any one of them could recover from his surprise, Salar was already far away. He pushed forward without paying any attention to what went on around him—no fish would have dared attack such a giant—and without partaking of food. Since reaching the estuary he had not eaten or felt the pangs of hunger. He lived on the reserves he had gathered at sea—there were masses of fat around his internal organs—and these sufficed for the accumulation of seminal fluid as well. So the days went by.

If Salar could have looked at himself in a glass, only three weeks after his entrance into the river, he would have been shocked by the change in his appearance. His rainbow hues had disappeared; the silver was dull and dingy. But Salar would not really have been shocked, after all. His one wish was to push forward; the heavier the burden of his seed, the more powerfully he was impelled in the direction of the spawning ground. And yet his impulse suffered brief relapses. There were times when he felt absolutely nothing and was as long as a week in a sort of coma, near the piles of a bridge, in the deepest part of the river. Even so, he was not hungry. Small fish came inquisitively close to him and even rammed their heads against his side without rousing any reaction. Then all of a sudden a new discharge of his intermittently functioning thyroid whipped him into action, and again, for weeks on end, he traveled upstream.

When he came to the junction of the Loire and the Allier, he turned right as confidently as a motorist reading a directional sign. But how many miles still lay ahead, how many obstacles to overcome! Most important among them, as we have all been thinking, were the dams. From a considerable distance Salar perceived the ebullition of the falling water. He was quite alone now, in the turbulent current; all the other kinds of fish remained a safe distance downstream. But Salar swam on with all his strength, until he came to the churning water at the foot of the dam. And there he leaped. Is this the exact word? Did his muscles actually project him like a bullet out of the water and up over the dam? Such is very rarely the case; the salmon that attempts a leap of this kind usually falls back into the water. It appears from close observation of the salmon's approach to a dam that the spectacular single leap through the air is not the most effective way over. Most often, Salar swam to the very foot of the fall, raised his body and with a superhuman effort went right on swimming. In an almost vertical position, moving on the surface of the water, he managed by this supreme effort to clamber over a dam six feet or more high.

Once he had reached the milling waters above, there was no question of relaxing. For several yards he had to fight against the onrush of the river at the point where it approached the fall. But this struggle could not compare with the one he had put up just before, and the demon that was pushing him upstream made him at times quite insensible to fatigue. At this point, he would have died before giving up the battle. Indeed, salmon have been seen to die of asphyxiation at the foot of a dam which they have vainly tried a hundred times to leap over.

Occasionally some man-made contrivance helped him on his way: a fish ladder or a series of artificial channels, which divided and broke the impact of the falling water. At other times man put obstacles in his way. There was fishermen's bait, which he knew for a trap and passed by. But many of his companions were hooked, somewhere along the river.

They snapped at the bait, not because they were hungry but because they imagined that they were attacking a foe. This is proved by the fact that when they did take a bite out of some free-swimming smaller fish they did not stop to swallow it. In their state of frenzied excitement, any object that crossed their path caused the reflex action of biting.

Thus it was, passing from one tributary to another, that Salar came to the mountain stream, which ran below summits crowned with snow. For almost a year he had had no food. His head had narrowed, and his enlarged lower jaw formed something like a hooked beak. His coat showed traces of pigmentary excretion, and his skin was loose and baggy. Still, Salar had lost none of his dynamic power. As he approached the goal he became progressively more excited.

When he came to the spawning ground and saw a female, larger than himself, rubbing her belly against the fine pebbles of the stream bed, he followed her resolutely, thrusting his male rivals out of the way. Nothing in all the world existed, except this egg-laying female. Even if you or I had stood on the shore or in the water, brandishing a pitchfork in one hand, it would not have deterred him. He would have let himself be killed on the spot rather than give up the accomplishment of the act which had brought him, through so many obstacles and dangers, all the long way from the sea. He would have died rather than fail to carry out his mission. Fortunately, no man stood in the swirling, icy water, brandishing a pitchfork in his hand. In the space of a single second Salar performed his life-giving work. Then, immediately, he relaxed and let the current bear him away. The female did likewise.

"Kelt" is the name given to the salmon after the act of

spawning, when he drifts inertly, tail first, or any which way, down the stream. He drifts from one tributary to another, without having to pick his route, because the destination to which the current, first impetuously and then deliberately and majestically, carries him is the sea.

Not all the salmon will arrive; far from it. Many of them, as the river rounds a curve, will be cast up on the bank and make a meal for some prowling animal. Others will be spooned up by a passing boatman from the surface of the water. "Look at that, will you? It's a kelt!" Some may recover a minimum of vitality, stop drifting, and swim to a calm inlet, there to wait for the coming of spring. Then, having more fully recuperated, they complete the journey with a greater chance of survival and join companions that have drifted, without untoward incident, all the way to the sea. Among these survivors, the older salmon are the least numerous. They have come nearer to fulfilling Nature's plan and the species needs them no longer. Some go on living, however, and there is nothing to prevent us from imagining that Salar is among them.

"The glad waters of the dark blue sea . . ." In this inexhaustible reservoir of energy the surviving kelts bathe as if in the fountain of youth. Appetite, strength, and color all return; they swim far out, dive under the curling waves and pursue their prey. Only two years later does the demon reawaken and call them back to the spawning ground. Some salmon accomplish the complete cycle as many as three times. But these are rare. Nature wants this lordly fish to conserve a full measure of its magnificent power, vitality and courage, and the individual that cannot transmit the heritage intact is doomed to perish.

3

Eels. . . . Is there really something to add to their often told story? I say that there is, quite definitely. Today in biology, almost every theory that was accepted not so many years ago is outdated, or else receives an entirely different interpretation. Imagine the adventure of the eels as a picture hung in a dark room and lit by a single candle. Suddenly the room is flooded with electric light; but parts of the picture are still shadowy and mysterious. . . .

I must have been only six or seven years old, and yet I can still see the scene and hear the words that were spoken. I had had some childhood illness, and my parents had sent me to convalesce on a Norman farm. I was happy except for one thing: there was no river, and I loved to dabble in the water. I had to content myself with a little pond, in the middle of a field, behind the stable, and this was dried up. The cracked muddy bottom was littered with a few dead branches and in the middle there was an overturned rusty bucket. I can see it distinctly.

Several weeks after my arrival there was a heavy rain. When it stopped and I went to look at the pond I found enough water to submerge the bucket almost completely. I remember vividly how startled I was when one of the dead branches, still stuck in the mud near the edge, suddenly uncoiled, glided nimbly and rapidly into the water and slithered across to the other side. Pharaoh could not have been so discomfited when Aaron's rod transformed itself before his eyes into a serpent! I ran back to the house, calling out: "A snake!" My excitement was so contagious that the farmer's sons ran to the pond with sticks and shovels.

"It's an eel!" they said as they waded into the water. "And what a beauty!"

With pounding heart I looked on at the capture. The olive-colored eel continued to slither from one side to the other, and when it was cornered it twisted its body out of the water and tried to elude the weapons of its pursuers. But it was no use; in a few minutes it lay, headless, on the green grass, with its yard-long body still writhing. That evening the farmer's wife made it into a steaming chowder. And I pressed them with questions about this snake that wasn't a snake at all. Between mouthfuls the farmer told me:

"There used to be plenty of them, down in the Iton River. They live in the water, but every now and then they come up on land. Only the little ones stay behind. Sometimes, when you cut up a big eel you find it full of crawling worms. . . . It all depends on the season. They come out of the water at night to mate with snakes."

His wife tapped his foot under the table and cast a severe look around her. Needless to say, I had asked enough embarrassing questions about the barnyard animals already. I wasn't at all sure what was meant by mating, and my ignorance made the farmer's sons chuckle. They would have laughed louder if they had known that the eel which they had just pulled out of their pond had been born in the ocean, nearly three thousand miles away. At the time—exactly forty years ago—no one knew exactly where eels were born. Their life cycle and reproductive habits were subjects of widespread and fantastic error.

The still incomplete discovery of the truth about eels is a detective story that reaches back over twenty-three centuries. But we can cover this ground in a very few minutes. Everything that antedates the century in which we are living can be set forth simply. We need only imagine a scholarly museum director, who by means of a machine for abolishing time and space can summon the wise men of the past to his office. The first to enter his door, coming from three hundred and fifty years before the Christian era, is Aristotle:

"The mullet goes up from the sea to marshes and rivers; the eels, on the contrary, make their way down from the marshes and rivers to the sea. . . . Eels are not the issue of pairing, neither are they oviparous; nor was an eel ever found with either milt or spawn, nor are they when cut open found to have within them passages for sperm or for eggs."

"Then how do you imagine that eels reproduce?" the museum director asks him.

"In some standing pools . . . the eels appear again after a fall of rain. . . . Eels are derived from the so-called 'bowels of the earth' . . . especially where there is decayed matter."

This unfortunate, or at least obscure, answer has long been held against the Greek philosopher. "He apparently set forth the theory of the spontaneous generation of eels," although this is doubtless an error of interpretation. Léon Bertin, author of an exhaustive and still up-to-date book about eels and a widely recognized authority on the subject of fish in general, has examined the Greek text of Aristotle's *History of Animals* and *Treatise on the Generation of Animals* and concludes that Aristotle probably meant to say that eels are born of larvae. In any case, he was the first to establish the important fact of their migration to the sea. Today, as in Aristotle's time, the eggs and seminal fluid of eels are very seldom seen. And, finally, it is quite true that, with their high resistance to desiccation and asphyxia, they can lie inertly for prolonged periods in the mud and recover their vitality with the first rain. Aristotle saw a number of points clearly. He was a keen observer and a true naturalist; he had nothing in common with the second visitor to penetrate our museum director's office, Caius Plinius Secundus, known as Pliny the Elder, a facile, hasty, and opinionated fellow:

"Lampreys are commonly believed to be inpregnated by copulating with snakes. . . . Tasting vinegar drives them mad." (The lamprey is a fish confused in ancient times with the eel.)

We shall not ask him to enlarge upon these statements, for fear of his unloading the full weight of his thirty-seven volumes upon us. Let us rather introduce—with regret at not letting him hold the floor longer!—Oppian of Cilicia, a poet of the second century. The object of his report is love among the lampreys.

> "The lamprey, glowing with uncommon fires,
> The Earth-bred Serpent's purfled curls admires;
> He, no less kind, makes amorous returns,
> With equal love the grateful serpent burns.
> Fixed on the joy, he bounding shoots along,
> Erects his azure crest and darts his forky tongue . . .
> In cranny'd rocks, far from the washing tide,
> There leaves the Furies of his noxious teeth—"

"Excuse me," says the museum director, "but couldn't you talk in slightly more scientific language?"

"Impossible! I am a poet. No amount of detail is as significant as poetry. Allow me to go on:

> "His mate he calls with softly hissing sounds,
> She joyful hears and from the ocean bounds
> Swift as the bearded Arrow's Haft she flies
> To own her love and meet the Serpent's joys—"

"He hisses a love song, does he? Have you ever heard a snake do that?"

Here we must cut short the conversation, which obviously can come to no good end. From the declamation of Oppian (for further details see his *Aleuticon*) we need remember only the four words "from the ocean bounds." Centuries must go by before we hear this little sentence again. Meanwhile a procession of slippered savants of the thirteenth, fourteenth, and fifteenth centuries passes before us: "The evidence is definitive: eels are born of the bodies of animals which have died in ponds and rivers." And sixteenth century savants in pleated ruffs: "If we throw into a shallow, muddy pond some hairs from the mane of a stallion, eels will be born of them." Theories multiply without anything worth listening to, until one day a messenger lays on our museum director's table a chapter from the works of Francesco Redi, a gentleman of Tuscany:

"As a result of extensive observation I am in a position to state that each year, on the darkest and cloudiest nights after the first August rains, eels start to travel in groups from rivers and lakes down to the sea. There they deposit their eggs; and, after a period of time which varies according to the rigor of the season, the young make their way through the river estuaries and into the fresh water upstream."

This text dates from 1684. A great step in the direction of the truth has been taken. Francesco Redi accurately described the eel's life cycle: migration of the adult eels toward the sea, the place where their eggs are deposited and matured, and return of the young eels to fresh water. In the same work he correctly identified as parasites the quantity of small worms often found in an adult eel's body.

But one question raised by Aristotle remained obscure:

"Nor was an eel ever found with either milt or spawn." Of course, Aristotle had no microscope. Later searchers learned to use this instrument more and more intelligently. The ovaries of the eel were identified in 1774 by Professor Mondini of the University of Bologna, and the male organs by a Pole called Syrski, director of the Museum of Trieste. But outside the scientific world extravagant stories continued to circulate. The farmer of my childhood and others of his kind continued to talk about the coupling of eels and snakes, a sight at which they gazed, on moonlit nights, with due horror and fascination.

When many scientists work long and simultaneously on the same subject, discoveries come thick and fast and overlap one another. In 1856 the German Krauss described a curious little creature he had caught in the Strait of Messina, four inches long, transparent as glass, flat and pointed at both ends like a laurel leaf. He gave the name of *Leptocephalus brevirostris* to this unknown or at least uncatalogued fish. Thirty years later two Italian ichthyologists, Grassi and Calandruccio, caught other specimens in the same place and proceeded to study them.

"These are eel larvae," they concluded. "Let us raise them in an aquarium and see."

Sure enough, the leptocephali turned into eels. Obviously eels reproduced themselves in the sea, since their earliest form was that of a marine larva. Everything was perfectly clear.

"No," someone objected. "Exactly where in the sea are they born?"

It doesn't matter who first raised the question, for it was one that everybody concerned with eels, including mere fishermen, was asking. From a psychological point of view, this widespread curiosity is very arresting. Salmon leave their native stream in order to live and grow in some region—no one is sure exactly which—of the sea. No excessive effort is expended in finding out if and where they all come together. We know where they are born and how they die, and the rest doesn't really matter. They have a perfect right to absent themselves and take a vacation. But if people don't know *where you come from*, that's a different matter. The neighbors, the doorman, the police, all are apt to investigate. So it was that the investigation of eels continued.

You may have noticed that we have left the office of our museum director. Twenty centuries in a museum is quite enough. Our detective story is going to acquire a more active and outdoor character and to continue aboard ship.

We are in the North Atlantic, between Scotland and Iceland; on the horizon there is the misty broken line of the Faeroe Islands. Our ship is the *Thor*, and it is flying the Danish flag. The pocket just now beginning to appear off the stern, at the end of a hawser which the crew is pulling in with the aid of a capstan, is no ordinary piece of fishing apparatus; it is a particularly fine net. No sooner is it hoisted on board than the crew empty it, not only of fish, large and small, which they throw into the hold, but also of a mass of minute living matter—the eggs and larvae of herring, mackerel, plaice, and many others—which is carefully preserved in buckets. A young man with a distinguished and intelligent face and dark, curly hair (I have his photograph before me) is closely watching the operation. It is not the captain, but Johannes Schmidt, a biologist and oceanographer, charged by the government of Denmark with the study of edible fish in northern waters.

Once the net is empty the twenty-seven-year-old scientist

goes down to his cabin-laboratory to examine and make notes on the contents of the buckets: the time and depth of the catch, the number and size of the specimens. This sort of study has to be accurate down to the slightest detail. Suddenly Johannes Schmidt stands very still and appears to be entirely absorbed by something he has just seen. There can be no mistake about it: this four-inch-long, transparent creature, flat and pointed at both ends, which he has picked out from the other larvae, is a leptocephalus, the first to be caught outside the Strait of Messina.

No other specimen was netted in the course of this year's expedition. But the discovery seemed to the Danish government commission to be so important that it told Johannes Schmidt:

"This is your job from now on: to discover where European eels deposit their eggs."

"I accept," the young scientist replied. But he wrote later: "I hadn't the slightest idea of all the difficulties involved."

In 1905, navigating farther south, the *Thor* netted several hundred leptocephali. Some of them, Schmidt found to be in the process of metamorphosis. Although they were still recognizable, they were beginning to acquire pigmentation; in certain cases they had begun to lose their flat, leaflike shape and to be slightly cylindrical. None of these larvae or semi-larvae were caught in the North Sea or the English Channel; they all were netted within thirty-two hundred feet below the surface. Schmidt came to this first conclusion:

"Eels reproduce far out at sea."

A third expedition, in 1906, yielded the same results. Schmidt, remaining on land, examined thousands and thousands of baby eels under the microscope.

"They all belong to the same species," he declared. "And

that is very significant. If there were several varieties, we might conclude that they reproduce in different places. But their sameness induces me to believe that they all come from a single spawning ground, and that this is far out in the Atlantic. Evactly where, I am responsible for discovering. Eventually I shall learn. Meanwhile, my next expedition will be to the Mediterranean."

Here is a surprise: Why the Mediterranean, when the conjectured spawning ground was in the Atlantic? But we shall see that Schmidt had a very definite idea, one not in the least silly but, on the contrary, highly logical and scientific. For two years between 1908 and 1910, the *Thor* cruised in the Mediterranean, dragging its extra-fine net behind it. Numerous leptocephali were caught, and Schmidt found out something which he had doubtless already suspected: only large specimens were to be found in this sea, and they were progressively larger as he moved eastward from the Strait of Gilbraltar. From this fact Schmidt drew a third conclusion:

"All the Mediterranean eels come from the Atlantic. I was correct in my theory that all eels are spawned in the ocean. If any were born in the Mediterranean, the very smallest specimens would obviously be found there. And they are not to be found at all."

Here occurred an interesting example of national susceptibility. Schmidt's words aroused great commotion. Italian naturalists protested, in a body, first among them Grassi, whom we have already quoted.

"Our eel cannot possibly come from the Atlantic," he insisted. "If Mr. Schmidt has not found small larvae in our waters, then he has not known where to look for them, or else his net is not sufficiently fine."

"If there were anything wrong with my net, then how does

it come about that I caught the minute larvae and even the eggs of so many other fish?" the Dane answered calmly. "If there is another explanation than mine, let it be presented."

While the Italians were at work on a countertheory supporting the birth of eels within the *Mare nostrum*, a Norwegian ship, the *Michael Sars*, brought to Europe leptocephali smaller than any that had ever been seen before. They had been gathered off the Azores Islands.

"The Azores?" exclaimed Schmidt. "I think that we're getting very warm. But I can't continue my research all alone. Won't some of my countrymen help me?"

Twenty-three Danish fishing captains answered his call and started dragging a fine net. Smaller and smaller leptocephali were caught. Meanwhile Schmidt, aboard a new vessel, the *Margrethe*, was combing the Atlantic from the Faeroe Islands to the Azores and from the Azores to Newfoundland, and then down to the Antilles. In 1913 the *Margrethe* foundered; but fortunately both the crew and Schmidt's precious collection were saved. And when the collection was evaluated it turned out that the smallest leptocephali of all, the closest to the egg, had been caught in the Sargasso Sea. The spawning ground of the European eels had been found. But the cautious Schmidt waited until 1920 to announce his discovery.

In olden days, sailing craft that entered the Sargasso Sea never got out of it. Most of the time there was not enough wind even to flap the sails, and when a faint breeze did stir, the mass of sargasso weed was too thick for a keel to move through it. The ship was a captive, and its crew knew that they were doomed to die of thirst. So legend had it. But the legend was false, or rather it was based on highly exaggerated stories. It is true that the Sargasso Sea contains the greatest accumulation of seaweed in the world. The American oceanographer A. E. Parr has estimated its total weight as ten million tons. But this mass is spread out, both horizontally and vertically, over an area almost as large as the United States, so that there are only a very few places where a sailing ship might be imprisoned.

Imagine an oval with its main axis stretching from just west of the Bermudas to the center of the Atlantic. It is encircled by the great ocean currents, and the winds are deflected; there are few clouds overhead and hence little rain. The intensity of the sunlight, the rapid evaporation, and the distance from any river make the water saltier than anywhere else. In this culture medium are great clumps of seaweed torn away by storms from the coasts of Florida and the Antilles and brought hither by the Gulf Stream. Here they float, without support or attachment, multiplying by fragmentation; and, once they have reached the dead center, where there is no current at all, there is no reason why they should not live forever. "It might well be," writes Rachel Carson, "that some of the very weeds you would see if you visited the place today were seen by Columbus and his men." Along with the seaweed, and to some extent borne by it, come numberless tiny sea creatures, larvae and very small fish, many of which adapt themselves to existence in the highly saline, motionless water. All sorts of shellfish are attached to the floating vegetation, while crustaceans and other creatures inhabit it, each species at the depth most propitious to it, suspended above abysses of two to three miles of water.

Such is the eel's cradle.

In Europe warm air announced the arrival of spring. Buds burst open and green wheat stood high in the fields. Men shook off their winter sluggishness, birds sang, and male and female animals sought out one another.

In the Sargasso Sea, thirteen hundred feet below the surface, at the limit of penetration by sunlight, where the temperature was about 62 degrees, every female eel had just laid between six and eight million eggs. (As many as this have been found in eel ovaries.)

The period of incubation was beginning. The eggs did not drop into the icy abyss, because each one contained several minute drops of oil which enabled it to maintain its level. There they hung, amid the seaweed, in their marine incubator. A few weeks later, when the quarter-of-an-inch-long larvae emerged, they too were kept from sinking by a drop of oil in the yolk sac which was to nourish them until they could stalk their prey. Not only were they saved from sinking, but soon they began slowly to rise to the surface. First a thousand, then eight hundred feet. Now the eel larvae belonged to that incomparably large, heterogeneous animal and vegetal population known as plankton, which winds its snakelike way through the seas all around the globe, coloring the surface according to its own composition. It gives food to whales and many other creatures of the sea, and as Alain Bombard proved in voluntarily living the life of a castaway, it can nourish a human being as well. The millions of creatures of which plankton is composed actually feed on one another. Salt-water shrimp, worms, and various small crustaceans eat the vegetal matter and are, in their turn, devoured by other creatures hardly larger than themselves. Plankton endures and flourishes autonomously.

The leptocephali rose within 100 feet of the surface at

night and then went back below 160 feet by day. Every one of them was transparent as glass, flat and pointed at both ends like a laurel leaf. At one end two black spots were the eyes. Even without a microscope it would have been possible to make out the regular succession of muscular segments, corresponding to the future 115 vertebrae of the spinal column. "Leptocephalus" means narrow-headed; but the narrow head was split by a real mouth, armed with sharp teeth. These were not strong enough to hurt a human being, but they were useful in the capture and mastication of their minute prey.

The length was still only two to three tenths of an inch, and the weight was almost imperceptible. The very slightest movement of the water was sufficient to displace such small bodies, and every day billions of leptocephali spread out in every direction, toward the periphery of the Sargasso Sea, where branches of the great ocean currents began to move them more rapidly. In choosing a current the leptocephali had to exercise considerable care. The cold current from Labrador and the warm one from the equatorial zone would be equally fatal to them. Other currents moving westward, toward the American coast, were no more healthy. Leptocephali that let these carry them away would reach the shore much too early, when they had barely completed a third of their larval growth; and, unadapted to the surroundings, they would perish.

Here a parenthesis is in order. There are, of course, North American eels: they abound in many large and small rivers. These, like the eels fated to travel to Europe, are born in the Sargasso Sea: but for them a westward current is imperative. "The question is," as an English naturalist recently put it, "How do the eel larvae manage to separate, some of them

to follow an eastward and others a westward route?"
Here is the answer: American eels are born toward the
western side of the Sargasso Sea. It is true that the two
spawning grounds partly adjoin each other; but the important fact is that the two varieties of eels are not sisters but
cousins: *Anguilla anguilla* (European) and *Anguilla rostrata*
(American). *Anguilla rostrata* has fewer vertebrae and attains its full growth more rapidly. This difference largely accounts for the separation. We may wonder how each tiny
larva can be aware that it belongs to one kind or the other,
but the wonder holds good for almost any animal. A lion
and a mouse may not be conscious of their difference, but
none the less each one acts on the supposition. Let us close
the parenthesis and return to the European eels.

Only by using the Gulf Stream, which would carry them
in a northeasterly direction, was it possible for them to survive. It must be admitted that the simple and satisfying
picture of the eels carried along by the great current has
been blurred by Le Danois's discovery of the transgressive
waters, already mentioned. It would not be the Gulf Stream
but these tropical transgressives that would carry the larvae
to Europe. The question is still a moot one. In any case, the
great troop of leptocephali, mingled with an infinite number
of other tiny creatures, diminishes every minute of every
day, through the cannibalism which, as we have seen, is the
social norm of the plankton.

Whole months went by. The migrating leptocephali ate
and breathed, while their organs continued to develop. Their
longitudinal fin consisting of rays became increasingly visible.
Everything pointed toward the arrival of a moment when the
eels would cease being carried passively along and start to
move under their own steam. Only an eel could recognize

the arrival of that moment. Autumn, winter, and a new spring had come, while the exodus to the northeast continued. The journey of the leptocephali was to last two and a half years.

From the continent of Europe reaches out a shelf which slopes gradually into the sea, as deep as a thousand feet, varying considerably in width in different places. After reaching this depth the bottom falls abruptly to depths as great as three thousand to six thousand feet. When the leptocephali reached this point, in the third autumn after their birth, they changed radically, in both appearance and behavior. Their teeth fell out, and they stopped eating. From flat laurel leaves they turned into slender, but still transparent cyclinders; and they substituted for their Latin name that of elver, or "glass eel."

Fishermen who net eels at this period of their migration, when they are so fat and pretty, supply many a table in Spain and southwestern France with the ingredients of a tasty fish fry or pâté. But they have to be caught at just the right moment, for in the next few weeks those that slip through the nets lose size and weight on account of their toothlessness, although they continue to aim unerringly at the coast.

What instinct or desire impels them? We come back to the fundamental problem of migration. "Every animal fits its way of living to the successive needs of its organism and moves through its natural environment in such a way as to satisfy the most pressing of these needs." And is there no more to say? The search for oxygen—the branchiotropism we have considered in connection with salmon—was long held responsible for the eels' migratory impulse as well. It is true that larvae need more and more oxygen as they grow, and that young eels travel from the highly saline Sargasso Sea to the fresh river water. Like the salmon, however, they make first for the estuaries, where the oxygen content of the water has been proved to be low. And so branchiotropism is not the answer. "The determining factor of the eel's metamorphosis appears to be a hormone from the thyroid gland," writes Léon Bertin. The thyroid again! Until further notice we may assume that the thyroid is responsible both for the larva's change of shape and for its impulse to travel. The two phenomena are linked closely together.

Most of the eels reach the European coast between October and March, the local dates varying with the breadth of the continental shelf. Since losing their teeth as leptocephali at the beginning of their metamorphosis they have grown a new and permanent set, shorter but at the same time more solid. With the increased ability to eat, they gain strength and agility. When conditions are favorable, they embark on a mass movement up the river, one of the most spectacular phenomena of animal life.

Off the estuary the sun has just risen over a rough sea. The swarming movement of the young eels causes the water to seethe as if it might at any minute boil over. More eels are constantly arriving; they pass over the sea, holding on to one another. Before our eyes is a weird sight: a white ball, over three feet in diameter, of clinging eels, which moves up and down in the water. Eels detach themselves from this as if it were an unwinding ball of wool, and form themselves into a long strand or rope which makes its way up the river, steadily reenforced by new arrivals.

The eel rope may be several miles long, three feet wide and eighteen inches thick. As the morning wears on, it gradually diminishes; the eels break away, slip into the mud or hide under pebbles. Although they have never seen a river before, they know how they must behave for survival. At night the rope takes shape again and pushes forward. Obviously, it is a practical application of the motto, "In union there is strength," for it can overcome a current which would carry a single eel back to the sea.

There are coastal localities where some obstacle makes the formation of such a rope impossible. Even so, the eels must make their way up the river. The famous nineteenth-century British physicist, Sir Humphry Davy, has described the eels' arrival in the Erne River, on the northwest coast of Ireland: "The mouth of the river, which had been in flood all this month, under the fall, was blackened by millions of little eels . . . urging their way up the moist rocks by the side of the fall. Thousands died but their bodies, remaining moist, served as the ladder for others to make their way." The eels' energy is invincible, and their migration might take on a positively nightmarish character, were it not that billions of larvae, in fact the greater part of those that leave the Sargasso Sea, perish within the moving mass of plankton, the vehicle which brings them hither. In a year, the railway stations of a single department of southwestern France, Landes, handle more than a hundred thousand pounds, that is, a hundred million eels.

Not all the eels join the armies that storm the rivers. Contingents of varying size remain in the estuaries or in near-by brackish ponds and lagoons. These shore-bound eels develop into males, while their more ambitious companions turn into females.

Let us be quite clear: the eels on arriving at the coast are neither males nor females; nor are they hermaphrodites, possessing complete or incomplete organs of both sexes; they are simply neuter, undifferentiated. Later, both groups go through a hermaphroditic stage, still without power to reproduce, because their sexual cells are not yet mature. None of them attains sexual maturity and reproductive power until the return to the sea. Such is a simplified account of the sexual evolution of eels. If now you understand how and why the shore eels—destined to pass (like the others) through the hermaphroditic stage before becoming (they alone) males— decide their future in separating from the others while the two groups are wholly undifferentiated and indistinguishable, if you understand this, send your explanation immediately to the Academy of Sciences at Paris: you can save precious time for the physiologists who are still dissecting eels in search of an answer. To enlighten you further, I may add that there are exceptions to the rule: occasionally female eels are found at the shore and males far from the sea. Leaving these nonconformists behind, let us follow the future females which with invincible will are pushing their way up from the sea.

Ascending the rivers and their affluents, the eels penetrate the smallest streams, and nothing stops them. They climb up the vertical walls of dams as if by holding on to them; at need they leave the water to circle other obstacles, gliding, like snakes, over the ground. Thus some of them stray into distant ponds, reservoirs, and even sewers. Eels from the Sargasso Sea have been found in the sewerage systems of large European cities and in the pipes that drain water from the subways. The conformation of their gills is such that they can store moisture, and the mucus secreted by their skin retards desiccation. For this reason they can stay hours and sometimes a day or two out of the water. Some eels go from pond to pond far in the interior. Peasants miles away from running or stagnant water have drawn up from a well enormous eels which had apparently been living and fattening there for years on end. No wonder so many fantastic stories have been woven about them!

The hollow between the two stones was eight inches below the surface of the river. Apoda's olive coat blended perfectly with the mud and the water plants: The silly little chubs swam lazily along the edge, without a thought in their heads. The first one to pass before the opening never knew what happened to him. Apoda's gastric juices were already at work. His fellows started to swim away; but Apoda wriggled quickly after them, and soon a second went the same way. Then she returned to her lair.

For all carnivorous river creatures life begins at night. Apoda's watery jungle extended no more than twenty-odd yards, but life there suited her perfectly. She was not at all like the "glass eel" she had been when she started to swim up the river. Her skin had acquired increasing coloration; now she was olive-green and yellow all over and ideally camouflaged. She was eight inches long, and was incredibly nimble and voracious. Almost any flesh was to her taste.

All day long she lay in the hollow. It was not that she was afraid—in the water she knew no fear; she was merely digesting. And during the hours when she lay low her menacing presence was quickly forgotten. Every morning the silly little fish swam lazily in front of her lair; all day long they were not molested, and when evening came she had only to snap her jaws around her first prey. Evening merged into night, and no moon relieved the blackness. But Apoda was quite able to detect her victims in the dark. The receptors of the nerve which ran the length of her body transmitted low-frequency vibrations far more efficiently than any radio apparatus. Long-distance soundings made her aware of the presence of any mobile object.

A few yards away a frog swam through the water. Apoda glided over the river mud and emerged on the bank. Across the near-by fields the lights of a farmhouse were shining. She crawled through the tall grass, then dived back into the water and proceeded along the edge. The little frog was there, croaking happily beneath the stars. Suddenly Apoda's pointed teeth were planted in its soft body. Reentering the stream, she ground it to pieces. Around her other eels were acting in exactly the same way; but Apoda took no interest in them. In her universe there was room only for Apoda and anything that could provide Apoda with food.

When winter came the water grew colder. Apoda had a presentiment that she was going to slacken her activity and rest. One evening, instead of watching for prey, she dived into the muddiest part of the stream and dug herself in. Bubbles of air rose to the surface, while she settled into a muddy refuge that was considerably warmer than the water.

A thin layer of ice formed on the apparently deserted banks. Farm chimneys smoked, and in the surrounding woods the peasants busily chopped down the trees. But the lethargic Apoda was no longer sensitive to this sound or any other. Time had a stop. Only in spring did the mud stir above the place where she was lying. Completely reanimated, she began to thrash about in the water.

So it went, year after year. When she was ten years old, Apoda was as much as sixteen inches long. The scales which had grown on her skin were an index to her age. Very few people suspect eels of having scales. One must look very carefully at their sticky, smooth skin in order to detect the mosaic pattern of tiny oblong spots placed at right angles one to another. Now Apoda left the water fearlessly in pursuit of frogs and toads in the meadows. She was still the picture of egotism, interested only in herself and her prey. She was just as carnivorous as ever, and increasingly powerful.

If you had killed Apoda at this time, and cut her into pieces, and then rubbed one of the pieces against a scratch or cut on your hand, the hand would have swollen and become inflamed, and you would have had a fever. If, as an experiment, you had injected eel's blood into the circulatory system of a rabbit, the rabbit would have gone immediately into convulsions, and its heart would have stopped beating. Although man can safely and agreeably eat eels, their blood serum is definitely toxic. This toxic quality makes the eel itself immune to most diseases and ensures its longevity. As country people would say, it flourishes like a weed.

How old was Apoda when the course of her life changed? Anywhere from thirteen to seventeeen—the exact age doesn't matter. In any case, one August she who had been so wrapped up in hunting and eating suddenly ceased to take an interest in either. Listless and inactive, she hung about, day after day, at the bottom of the stream. There are times when I can imagine for myself a life of this kind. But not without the impairment of my health; I should surely lose weight, and my idle digestive organs would suffer from disuse. Such was the case with Apoda. But her looks, instead of deteriorating as mine would surely do under the circumstances, altered advantageously. Her coat changed from olive-green and yellow to a shiny bronze, almost black, on the back and sides, while her belly turned silvery white, with reflections of

purple. The general tonality was no longer dull, but metalli-
cally bright and shining.

The reader doubtless remembers the transformation of
the young river salmon from parr to smolt, and here, indeed,
is a parallel. Once more the little interior demon that sparks
a change in neuroendocrinal activity had spoken. Having
brought about an alteration of the eel's appearance, he now
ordered her to travel.

Let us leave Apoda among the millions of her sisters, who
in autumn hear the same call. Not all hear it at the same age,
and many of those that hear it cannot answer. Think of the
eels that have buried themselves at the bottom of a well,
and of their vain efforts to emerge from it! Others may be
surprised in some pond by a sudden cold wave and find
themselves imprisoned under a sheet of ice. They can only
dig down deeper into the mud and postpone the journey
until the following year or the year after—that is, if the same
circumstances are repeated. Every spring these prisoners
start again to hunt and to stuff themselves. In many cases they
never make up their minds to choose a sex; they live like
eunuchs, growing progressively fatter and fatter until they
die of old age, unless they have been captured and cut into
pieces.

But for the others the exodus has begun. Everywhere, from
lakes and ponds, eels crawl through fields, around farm-
houses, and into the rivers, which are crowded now with con-
voys setting out for the sea. The sea is still distant; the
ultimate goal—the reproduction of the species—is surely in-
discernible to these travelers whose femininity will not become complete until they are well along the way; but they
have received the initial impulse, and nothing can halt
them. For two or three months groups of eels, some of them

wound two or three together, move downstream. Every now and then they meet younger eels moving in the opposite direction, but the two groups show no sign of greeting or recognition. Every tributary adds to the descending army. People living along the river have thrown up improvised dams and are hauling eels in by the netful. But such losses cannot decimate their ranks. Hundreds of millions, perhaps billions, of females escape all the snares laid for them and pour into the sea, each one bearing millions of eggs in her body.

Meanwhile the males, who have spent all this time in the estuary, or in the brackish ponds and lagoons near by, have also gone down to the sea. Look closely at these strong, supple snakes as they glide easily along, as easily as if all their life long they had never left salt water. Look closely, because you may never see them again. Now they have dived under the surface and disappeared. Far from the sun, far from all light, these snakelike fish with the narrow, pointed heads are progressing at a depth where the pressure would be far too great for man. Coming from the whole length of the European coast, from the White Sea to the southern tip of Spain, millions of long, pointed heads converge upon the oval area, forgotten by the winds, where millions of tons of seaweed have their home. This place has a magnetic attraction for them, and they do not stop to eat or rest until they have reached it.

I have neglected a whole category of migrants—the eels of the Mediterranean—who should be answering the roll-call at the Sargasso Sea, but instead, are absent. What a mistake it would be to leave them out! For their fate forms a strange, sterile footnote to that of their fellows. The Mediterranean eels are trapped by a sudden difference in the saline content

of the water at the Strait of Gibraltar, "which is as insur-
mountable a barrier as a high stone wall." But who would
object to having the Mediterranean for a prison? The prisoners
do not reproduce, but they have long and happy years
ahead of them. All the long pointed heads pushing their
way westward are doomed to die. For the cradle of the
species is also an extermination camp.

It is established beyond any doubt that eels reproduce in
the Sargasso Sea; and yet not a single adult eel has ever been
caught there. The only silver-bellied eel ever taken in the
mid-Atlantic was found in the stomach of a sperm whale,
which happened to be traveling along the route of migration.
The eels from the continent of Europe plunge into the sea and
are never seen again.

But the mind's eye can see them. Day after day, contingents of the vast army work their way through the ocean
depths to their final destination. Imagine the welter of
reproductive activity, the millions of bodies pressed close to
one another, entwined or perhaps stuck together in masses as
we have seen them when they started up the estuary, and
finally the cloud of newly created life, the billions of fecundated eggs drifting through the water. And this confusion
goes on for weeks and months, as more and more eels arrive,
males swollen with seed, females carrying as many as five or
ten million eggs, all of them excited to the highest degree by
the impulse that has driven them hither. They burst, free
themselves of their burden, and then . . .

Once more I see the limp bodies of the lordly salmon,
emptied and exhausted by the act of reproduction, having
often lost even the will to survive. The eels, whom no one has
ever seen again, surely they die in the very place where they
have just given life, immediately. The call which summoned

them from their Scottish river or pond Auvergne was one which they could not disobey; it imposed an almost unbearable tension upon them, and obviously it is impossible for them to live on, after the releasing spasm. They are among those of whom the Species demands everything. In the course of their journey their substance has been transformed into eggs and seed; when these are gone, what remains? A limp, snakelike creature, demineralized to the point where its bones are soft and almost spongy. In this condition, there is no hope of resuming the struggle for existence in the cold sea. And what could be the purpose of such an existence, after they have multiplied themselves a million times over? Until the very last minute the picture of egotism, interested in themselves alone, the eels descend now into the abyss, set forth upon their last journey to the absolute and icy shades.

CHAPTER III

THE BUFFALO TRAILS

The herd feeding on the plain made an incredibly peaceful picture. The great buffalo grazed and ruminated for all the world like Jersey or Guernsey cattle, the reddish yellow coats of the spring calves mingling with the uniform brown of the adults. The standing animals moved slowly, cropping the grass with machinelike regularity, while their ruminating companions lay with their feet tucked under them and their eyes closed, in an obviously beatific condition. The bucolic character of the scene was intensified by the presence of hundreds of tiny birds which hopped among their hoofs or still more trustingly perched on their broad backs and filled the air with their joyful chirping. These little friends were in charge of anti-insect defenses. Buffalo do not moo, like other bovines. Here and there a subdued rumble could be heard; but the prevailing sound was the chirping of the birds.

Suddenly one of the ruminating bulls jumped to his feet, and at once all the animals were standing. Any superficial resemblance to domestic cattle was gone. For the thousands of buffalo did not rise heavily and slowly from the ground; they leaped as if triggered by a spring, straightening all four legs simultaneously.

All the buffalo faced the same way, with their muzzles in the direction of the wind. After a few seconds a curious movement began. The herd did not change position, but individuals milled about. Then they stood perfectly still. But the calves had gathered in the center of the herd, and their mothers were around them, while the bulls mounted guard on the outer edge. The herd was in a state of active defense.

Buffalo have mediocre sight; but their hearing is keen, and their sense of smell exceptionally developed. What could the buffalo sense as they stood with their muzzles turned all in one direction? They did not raise and lower their heads nervously, as horses would have done. Turned toward the wind, but with no expression upon their faces, they stood as still as rocks on the plain, while the small birds continued to flutter and chirp among them. A long minute went by.

Finally one and then another buffalo moved. Some began to walk and to graze while others went back to ruminating. The calves and their mothers moved away, and the defense formation was broken. The alarm was over.

The American buffalo measures between sixty and seventy inches to the shoulder, and weighs nearly a ton. His skin, as we have seen, is dark brown. Just behind his neck is a hump formed by a prolongation of the dorsal vertebrae. But no detailed description can give any idea of his appearance if we fail to state the first impression he produces upon the beholder. Rather than an animal he appears to be a tree. No, a rock. When he is seen head on and motionless in the middle of the plain, he might be a rock or boulder. The massive forequarters bear down crushingly upon the ground, with the nose and forehead forming a vertical line. A pair of short horns rise from this monolithic block, and on either side of the head is a brown, expressionless eye, set into it like a bright stone.

Now the boulder has moved; the head has turned to one side, but still there is no expression in the eye. Has a thought traversed this craggy cranium? *Bison bison* raises his head slightly, and opens his jaws in a gaping yawn, which reveals a voluminous tongue of a beautiful dark slate color. This tongue has caused the death of thousands of bison, not on account of its color but on account of its taste. Now *Bison bison* closes his mouth and takes two or three steps forward. Anyone that sees a buffalo in motion for the first time cannot but be overpowered by the sight. He has neither the colossal mass of the elephant nor the majestic power of the lion, although he recalls them both; his motion suggests, rather, that of some enormous projectile. In the very first movement of his shoulder muscles he reveals an energy potential which defies comparison with any other living creature. Buffalo shut up behind high board fences have been known to submit, motionless, for months on end, to their captivity. Then one day, suddenly, inexplicably, they broke the boards with the ease with which you or I might crumple a folder of matches. When the buffalo turns his back to us, he shows a pair of bare, comparatively meager flanks. They are substantial enough, but the real power of the projectile is at the front end.

In the old days, when a herd of buffalo left its wintering place, the Indians discovered great circles traced deeply at regular intervals on the ground. Later, the white men saw them too and unable to explain their mystery called them "fairy rings." But the Indians knew that buffalo, not fairies, had traced them. Gray wolves, including some as big as donkeys, followed the herd a large part of the year. At the time when the calves were born and as long as they were awkward and helpless, the herd was in a state of defense, with the calves and their mothers in the middle and the bulls pacing around them. Day and night they kept watch, pacing in a perfect circle, whose deep trace was left behind them.

It is always surprising to see a whole civilization built around a single animal, and yet there are numerous examples: Eskimos live off the seal, and Laplanders off the reindeer; North American Indians, in their time, lived off the buffalo. To the first man and woman the Great Spirit said: "Here is the buffalo; he shall provide your food and clothes." And indeed the Indian coming back from the hunt wore buffalo moccasins, and shirt and leggings of tanned buffalo hide, while his family waited for him under a tent of the same material. A woolly buffalo robe provided a winter bed, and one with the hair removed served in summer. The warrior fashioned his shield from the thick skin around the neck, which was strong enough to deflect arrows; and the cord of his bow came from one of the animal's sinews. His squaw carried water in a buffalo's gut, and buffalo meat was undoubtedly the basic, most substantial, and easiest to preserve of all the Indian's food. It was also the most tasty—particularly, as has been suggested, the tongue, and the flesh of the hump. Buffalo hides formed skiffs for crossing rivers and light sleds for travel over the snow. Yes, the animal which the Great Spirit had given to man supplied his every need, including even magic power, for no "medicine" paint was as efficacious as that made out of pulverized stones from the buffalo's gall bladder.

Quite aside from the realm of "medicine" and magic, the buffalo inspired the Indians to cultivate the strength, courage, and skill required to hunt it. Before horses were introduced in the New World, the Indian strategy had been to capture the buffalo in traps or, at some risk, to drive them over steep cliffs. After learning to ride horseback, and to ride in incomparably masterful fashion, they attacked their prey with the lance or the bow and arrow, handling both with fantastic boldness and dexterity. Their hunting had a truly sporting character, for they ran definite risks in order to show their bravery. Moreover they never killed more animals than they needed. Why should they do so? The buffalo were always there, like the water in the springs and the light which the Great Spirit caused to rise in the sky every morning. To the Indians the buffalo was a sort of divinity, which gave them everything, which they killed but continued to surround with veneration.

The herd began to move in early summer, a few weeks after the birth of the calves. There was no preparation or forewarning; on the plains, to north, south, east and west, the grass was still abundant, and there seemed to be no urgent reason for departure. And yet, one morning . . .

At one end of the flock, farthest from the mountains that showed on the horizon, some bulls ceased grazing and began to move as if attracted by the wide, open space. First a few, then a few dozens and a few hundreds. Eventually this front line transmitted its movement to the rest. It seemed as if invisible messengers, blowing silent trumpets, were flying above them. "You there, you too, start moving, all of you, on the way!" The reddish yellow calves walked beside their mothers. Now the front line broke into a trot, and all the others trotted after. This was to be the normal gait during migration.

As the buffalo moved across the plain they did not hurry and push one another like a crowd in the subway. They proceeded in long lines, single file, each animal two feet behind the next. The lines started out parallel, but in a series of gradual, almost imperceptible shifts the calves and females came to occupy the center, while the bulls stayed on the outside. The safety measures to be taken during the long trek existed, in a very precise form, inside every one of these heavy heads, behind every rocklike forehead. Without a single grunt or any signal apprehensible to the eyes or ears of man, the herd of let us say twelve thousand buffalo maneuvered, flawlessly, into the correct position.

The buffalo trotted all day long, and in the evening they lay down on the plain, with their muzzles toward the wind. No living thing could pass in front of them without alerting their sense of smell, even if they happened to be sleeping. Wolves, aware of this fact, always tried to creep up on them against the wind. For protection from such an attack some of the buffalo remained on the watch, pacing up and down in a wide circle. The next morning the buffalo ate and chewed their cud before moving on. So it went, every day . . .

The herd proceeded as harmoniously as a broad river, with tributaries pouring in from either side. From time to time, one or more lines of other buffalo descended from the foothills. Heavy animals surer-footed than mules, they wound their way down the steep slopes and then galloped across the prairie to join the procession. Many of the new arrivals had managed to cover themselves with mud now dry and caked as a protection against giant mosquitoes and other insects.

The herd proceeded harmoniously; but the sight of the rear guard was one to inspire pity and horror. Here, in the dust raised by the animals that had gone ahead, tattered wrecks of buffalo trotted clumsily along. Some of them had lost not only patches of skin, but chunks of flesh, which attacking wolves had torn out of their hips and flanks. Eventually, in spite of their gaping wounds, they had managed to gore their assailants and rejoin the migrating herd. With an irregular gait and hanging heads (sometimes even an eye hung out of its socket) they tried desperately to keep up, knowing that another attack would be too much for them. Almost without exception these victims were forty or fifty years old. A rigid convention banished them to the rear, and they fatalistically accepted this position, which they shared with a few younger buffalo, handicapped by some accidental wound or temporary ailment. The wolves, of course, continued to attack from the rear. But the herd went on; there was no mercy for the old or unfit.

Yet, deep in some woodland valley a solitary old buffalo, miraculously preserved from this ferocious elimination, still wandered. Burdened with years, he had not sought to follow his companions who had gone to join the main body of the migrants. A strange fate and a terrible punishment were his: his greatest suffering was fear. The bull with the rocklike forehead, the killer formerly capable of goring a horse and carrying it on his horns for a hundred yards or more was pathologically afraid. He trod as cautiously as a doe, or a ghost; a crackling leaf or even the sight of his own shadow caused him to tremble. And who finally attacked him? Not a great gray wolf, but a coyote or some even smaller and more cowardly carnivorous animal. The law of natural selection was vindicated, for it was written that no buffalo should die of either illness or old age.

In 1871 an army of buffalo crossed the Arkansas River

between Fort Zarah and Fort Larned. The crossing took several days, for the army was fifty miles long and twenty-five miles wide. The witnesses who tried to count its numbers agreed upon the approximate figure of four million head. At the apex of their numerical strength there were between fifty and seventy million buffalo on the continent of North America.

Eyewitnesses to the great herds' migration had the sight indelibly impressed upon their memory. When the buffalo went through a valley they filled it from one side to the other, forming a homogeneous, unbroken rolling carpet which stretched all the way to the horizon and advanced as inexorably as a flow of lava.

In reading western stories one gets the impression that the vast area between Canada and the Mexican border, the Appalachian and the Rocky Mountains, was constantly overrun by migrating buffalo, whose movements seem to have had a highly illogical pattern. In the eastern part of this area, they are said to have traveled from north to south and back, while farther west their course was transversal. "When summer comes, the buffalo leave the wooded foothills which have protected them from the icy winter wind and go to graze on the grass of the plains." And yet we read of herds setting out in the dead of winter, amid a heavy snowstorm, and also of buffalo which apparently left the plains in the middle of summer and started over the barren mountains. The men on whom we must rely for our account of the American buffalo were not interested in the scientific aspect of animal migration.

And yet the buffalo always followed the same itinerary. A variation in the color of the grass indicated their passage across the plains. The earth trodden by their hoofs and enriched by their dung was more fertile than the rest. The buffalo has left an enduring mark on the American landscape, at least as long as men travel on the ground. The engineers responsible for plotting the routes of the Baltimore & Ohio and Union Pacific railroads worked out with the aid of relief maps the most economic and efficient way of crossing first the plains and then the mountains. Later when topographers went to look over the terrain, they found that almost everywhere the projected railway route followed the thousand-year-old trail of the buffalo.

The buffalo caught the smell of water and quickened their trot. For days they had been marching through dust and heat; in many places the grass was already yellow and sere. A cloud of dust rose around them, sticking to their hair and penetrating their eyes. They detected the water five miles away and rejoiced in it. Such a body of water would permit them to drink their fill, wash themselves clean, and then wallow in the mud of the banks clothing themselves with a protective garment against insects. In short, it offered them every possible pleasure. When they were about a mile from the river, the little birds took off from their backs and flew ahead. They were suffering from thirst even more than the buffalo. The river, which curved a little here, was about four hundred yards wide. To be more exact, its high banks were four hundred yards apart. The water was low and occupied a channel of something over a hundred yards near the farther shore. Between this channel and the buffalo was an expanse of mud—hard, white, and cracked near the bank, soft and black near the water. The tiny feet of thousands of birds had already left a sharply outlined pattern upon it.

The smell of the water was overpoweringly attractive, and

the buffalo had begun to gallop. Three-quarters of a mile long and at least three hundred yards wide, the herd galloped in parallel lines, which drew closer together, as they habitually did when a definite objective was in view. The river bank was not too high, and the first buffalo to reach it went on without pause, their hoofs ringing on the caked mud. But a hundred yards farther along, the mud was no longer firm enough to carry the ton of a buffalo's weight. Everywhere, the brown legs sank into it.

The tens of thousands of buffalo rushing toward the water were like so many speeding locomotives. The first arrivals did not have time even to think of extricating themselves before the next tumbled them over and went on, only to sink into the mud themselves a few feet beyond. The mad charge was indescribable. The herd threw itself at the water, trampling down members that were in the way. Those who finally got there had to pass over a compact mass of their mired companions. Not all of these were dead; many still groaned and struggled to hoist themselves on the shoulders of others, only to slip, fall back, and recommence the agonizing struggle. Those who had trampled them down in order to reach the water did not look back. They swam tranquilly to the opposite bank, climbed out, and then turned around to drink. The herd—that is, the survivors—then lay down to rest. It was plain that they intended to stay a few days and enjoy the water. They were not in the least distressed by the sight of thousands of dead and dying, soon to be putrefying corpses.

It is impossible to say how many buffalo would have survived had the river channel been in the middle of the mud flats instead of up against the farther shore. Perhaps the whole herd would have perished. From time to time such a sacrifice was necessary in order to maintain the number of buffalo in proper balance and preserve the grandeur of the race. A surplus of buffalo would have meant: "We no longer have enough grass to eat, and so we are becoming punier than our ancestors." The Great Spirit did not wish this to happen, and yet neither the wolves' nor the Indians' depredations could prevent it.

As soon as the buffalo reached their summer pastures, the single combats began. Strange as it may seem at first glance, the buffalo which lived in freedom on the plains fought much less frequently and ferociously than the few survivors in enclosures today. The wide, open space around them and the great number of cows made it unnecessary for the bulls to clash with one another. And yet from time to time, in accord with the law of natural selection, they fought.

Like the fights between fur seals of the North Pacific, the combats between buffalo have often been described inexactly. The adversaries have been shown hurling themselves at each other like cannon balls, from a distance of fifty to a hundred yards, and bringing their heads explosively together so that their skulls burst open. A careful reading of eyewitness accounts and current observation of captive buffalo prove that reality was altogether different from these romantic descriptions. Less spectacular, but just as impressive, in spite of a much slower tempo.

Around one of the buffalo, the space has emptied, and he is scraping the ground with his hoof like any other threatening bovine. But his bellowing is not like any other; it is deep and strangely guttural and seems to come out of the earth. A similar bellowing can be heard from twenty yards away, where another bull is going through the same actions.

Both heads are lowered in the normal preparation for attack. The buffalo's weapons are his horns, through which his full weight is brought to bear. Strange to say, in this position he cannot see straight ahead: his eyes are too far to the side. That is why each of our buffalo turns his head in a comical manner, first to one side and then to the other in advancing, as if to make sure that his adversary is still there. From time to time he pauses, paws the ground, and bellows.

These slow, successive advances finally reduce the space between the animals' heads to about twenty inches. Then, simultaneously and with all their strength, they hurl themselves at each other.

At once the two massive bulks are immobilized. There is fascination in this very immobility. The straddling hoofs dig into the ground, but not very deep, because the two forces are so symmetrical that no vertical deviation is possible. If there were one, the two noses would crush each other on the ground or else the two one-ton masses would be catapulted simultaneously into the air. The muscles visible behind the mane, from the shoulders all the way to the tail, are sculptured blocks. Every now and then the buffalo breathe deeply; their enormous chests fall and rise together, as if there were some understanding between them. Is it a convention or merely a game? The total silence in which the duel takes place indicates that it is neither. There is no bellowing sound nor cry. Every ounce of vitality and force which the buffalo has accumulated in the course of his life is transformed into this pushing action. For the time being, the buffalo *is* this push, and nothing more. The two animals, locked in combat, give a good picture of nations engaged in what we call total war.

The taut, sculptured muscular apparatus which gives the first sign of weakening is almost always that of the loser.

There can be a sudden, last-minute reversal, but not very
often. The end usually comes in this fashion: a muscle trembles, and a leg gives way. The balance is broken, and the
loser is thrown to the ground, where the winner immediately
sinks his horns into the body. The winner might die from
congestion of the lungs or madness if he did not tear his
opponent to pieces on the spot. The brute force which he
has carried to a state of paroxysm must relax, somehow. Let
us add one thing: Many combats between young bulls are
mere trials of strength; only mature bulls duel to the death.

Winter comes to the plains in a gale of wind, wind from
the east, wind from the north. For several weeks the sky may
remain a pale, tender blue. Then one morning, half the sky
is white, and it is snowing. This is when the buffalo's robe
attains its greatest beauty. It is ragged at the beginning of
the spring and finally is shed, leaving the animal quite bare.
Then it grows out again, brown and heavy, like a sealskin.
A few light or dark gray and also cream-colored buffalo have
been seen, and some with blue overtones, the handsomest
of all.

When there is snow on the ground the buffalo search for
grass with their muzzles, and when the surface of lakes and
rivers is frozen over they break the ice by ramming their
heads against it, making a noise like that of ten thousand
bludgeons. Sometimes part of a herd falls through a hole in
the ice and disappears, but the rest crosses successfully. The
herd, powdered with snow, continues over the white plain.
On the backs of the buffalo there are no birds or insects, no
small winged companions. These have left the herd long
since, for their distant wintering places, and will not return
before spring.

The herd comes to a halt at the end of a short winter day, and the buffalo lie down in the snow, huddled together, their heads to the wind. The snowflakes fall on a multitude of outstretched statues, each tiny crystal melting almost as soon as it comes in contact with the animal body. Around the resting herd, the usual sentinels keep a pacing vigil.

For the wolves winter is a hard season. Many animals go underground, and those domesticated by man take shelter in stables or enclosures. There is snow as far as the eye can see, and yet the wolves must live, they must satisfy the hunger that they carry, like another animal, within them. Hunger is inherent in the wolf's very nature. His organism is a great consumer of food, and except in periods of disorder or catastrophe he can never find enough to satisfy it. Wolves would be much more numerous if many of them did not die of starvation, if they were not so often reduced to cannibalism. It is a fact that wolves eat one another.

The wolves crouched in the snow, less than a hundred yards from the herd. They knew that the buffalo would not attack them and they could sleep peacefully close to these giants with the death-dealing horns. But of course none of them slept; hunger kept them all awake. The snow-laden wind blew the warm, animal odor of the buffalo in their direction; they bathed in this odor as if it were an intoxicating river and their appetites were further exasperated.

The wolves lay in the snow, with all their muzzles turned toward the buffalo. Unlike them, they were far from resembling statues; they lay tensely in the cold, with their forefeet stretched out, their noses raised to sniff, and their lips curled, from time to time howling. They knew that it was no use, even at night, to try to penetrate the resting buffalo's defenses. They must wait until the moment of departure. The herd started out at dawn, assuming within a few minutes its regular traveling formation. The wolves attacked almost immediately. A few highly excited wolves rushed forward and penetrated the guard, while the rest followed, howling. The attack did not last long. The herd moved on, leaving behind a wolf's body, covered with blood, the stomach ripped open. At once the wolves fought over it. Here was their weakness: a single body of one of their own was enough to distract them from the attack and demoralize them.

Half an hour later, sticking close together, they attacked again, this time successfully. A buffalo in the last line turned when they nipped his flanks and began to go after them with his horns. Unfortunately no wolf was in his path, and the pack continued to howl around him. He charged again, and again missed his aim, as the wolves pulled away on either side. He made a half-turn, obviously to rejoin the herd, but there were wolves in his path, and he had to charge them. Once more they pulled away, and at the same time teeth sank into his legs from the rear. He wheeled around, throwing the wolves off and with them shreds of flesh which they tore off his bleeding flanks. Again he charged at the wolves he saw before him. Meanwhile the herd trotted away over the snow. Already it was some distance off. Again the buffalo charged at the wolves in the direction of the retreating herd, in order to break through them and catch up with his fellows. But the wolves repeated their former maneuver. They had succeeded in isolating him.

And yet this buffalo did not look at all as if he had been trapped and were doomed to die. He charged the wolves, first at one side and then the other, and they gave way; but, each time, they described a circle and came back at him from the rear. Meanwhile, strangely enough, he seemed to have forgotten the herd. He was annoyed with the wolves; his chief aim was to shake them off, and so he continued to charge. And they, like the picadors in a bull fight, dodged him, unerringly.

Less than half an hour after the separation from his fellows, the buffalo ripped two wolves to pieces and thus obtained a good chance to rest. Each of the corpses became the center of a confused and madly howling pack of wolves. Could he not have taken advantage of this respite to rejoin the herd? Perhaps so. But all he did was to withdraw a very slight distance, holding at bay the few wolves which had been unable to get anywhere near the bodies and were still badgering him. For a few seconds he even burrowed with his muzzle in the snow. The ugly wounds on his flanks seemed not to disturb him.

Apparently not one of the wolves was able to eat his fill, for a few minutes later they all once more surrounded the buffalo, and the bull fight was resumed. It was prolonged, over and over, by the buffalo's triumph over a single one of his adversaries. Every time this happened he managed to recoup some of his strength and charge them with renewed vigor. Although he was one against many, he actually exhausted them. Some of the wolves crouched in the snow, panting and licking the blood from their fur. The day was fast waning.

Not even a champion can battle for hours at the peak of efficiency, and this rear-guard buffalo was no longer young. Eventually his charges came to resemble the jerky advance of a superannuated bus rather than the bee line of a racer. Forward, to either side and about-face he thrust his massive body, shaking his heavy head close to the ground, with his beard in the snow. He had lost one eye, and a whole side of his face was bitten down to the cartilage. The ragged ribbons trailing in the snow were strips of skin from his legs, and the white object protruding under the hip was the femur, exposed to the air.

At last the buffalo disappeared from view, eclipsed by wolves which had thrown themselves, all together, upon him. But the swarm of wolves was not motionless, it moved as if it were being dragged along; suddenly it was shaken, and some of its members fell off on either side, while a monstrosity, once a buffalo, incredibly charged again. Then the wolves once more threw themselves upon him. Any one of us would have been glad to take a gun and put an end to this butchery; but, with nothing that we can do, we had best avert our gaze and go away.

A single isolated buffalo is known to have fought all day against a pack of wolves, and one that could buttress himself against a rock or cliff was able to hold out considerably longer. But, unless some hunter intervened, he always came to the same abominable end. A squirrel, caught by the iron jaws of a wolf, has no time to suffer. But to the great of this earth, death may bring considerable agony in its train.

The herd trotted on toward its winter pastures. The buffalo are strange migrants. In spite of being mammals, they seem more remote from man than salmon. Did the adults have in mind some image of the plains toward which they were going, so often similar to those they had left behind? What impulse set them in motion when there was still no lack of fodder around them? Did some glandular modification make them sensitive, like other migrants, to a cosmic command? The great buffalo herds no longer exist, and when they did men took no interest in them except as game.

That year the winter was marked by early falls of heavy snow. In the great open spaces, one cannot properly speak of snow drifting down from the sky. Mention of snow implies a storm.

For two days such a snowstorm had been raging, characterized by violent wind, a uniformly gray sky and only a few yards of visibility. The wolves followed the herd at a distance of less than thirty feet, guided by smell. And what could the front line of buffalo see? Only a whirling mass of snow. How, then, were they guided? They did not choose their destination; they submitted to it. Amid our ignorance of the migrant buffalo's sense of direction, we can lay hold of one definite fact. Every time a snowstorm transformed the landscape with its white curtain, the buffalo spontaneously broke into a trot, pushing against the wind. They did not pause to wonder what they should do. The story I am about to tell is of a hundred thousand buffalo in 1858, and the same thing has happened to their kind many times in the course of the ages.

The buffalo trotted at first, and then broke into a sort of single-foot. Although this gait made the whole herd appear to limp, swaying from side to side, it rested them from the effort of breasting the snow. Eventually they slowed down to a walk. The snow stood higher and higher on the ground and swept more and more powerfully out of the sky. Moreover, night was about to fall. None of the buffalo knew the old stories of entire herds that had been found frozen to death in the snow, but many of them had lived through hard winters and had some inkling of the fact that the approaching night would be anything but gay. It was indeed a night of horror.

The instinct of self-preservation forbade the herd to stop,

much less to lie down. All night long they moved on, often fending the snow with their muscular chests. Needless to say, they moved very, very slowly, huddled all together. Behind, the wolves were so close that sometimes their muzzles touched the hind legs of the buffalo. In spite of gnawing hunger they had not the slightest urge to bite. The terrible and imperious snow would not allow them to waste a single motion outside the struggle to keep alive, to keep moving, for fear of being suffocated and buried in the darkness.

Through sheer obstinacy, the buffalo did not perish that night. When day broke the herd was still together, pushing against the snow. The sun must have been for some time above the horizon, but it was impossible to say exactly where, and the daylight was no brighter than dawn. Toward the middle of the day the storm diminished in fury and the snow stood less high on the ground, so that the buffalo could trot again. There was still snow in the air but there was a visibility of at least thirty feet, such as they had not enjoyed since early the preceding day. The hoofs of the leaders scattered the snow almost joyfully, and the rest of the herd quickened their pace to keep up.

What gave the front-line buffalo a warning? Did they perceive a different coloring in the wall of snow or a variation in its furious movements? At any rate, they slowed down, all together, or attempted to do so. Their legs stiffened, and there was something like a rip-tide in the snow tossed up from the ground. If there had been only one, or at most a few lines of buffalo, they might have cut down their speed before the precipice. But the pressure of the thousands of trotting locomotives behind them did not permit them to stop within the thirty feet of visibility ahead. Like a carpet, the whole herd rolled over the cliff. Nothing could avert the total catastrophe.

Perhaps some of the buffalo heard the noise produced by their predecessors, as they made the ninety-foot fall, one on top of another; but the wind was whistling loudly, and even if they had heard it, it is unlikely that they would have understood its meaning. We have already observed that buffalo, especially when they are traveling in herds, are not given to reflection. To the very last one, they tumbled over; there was nothing to stop them. Later, the gigantic pile of skeletons—spread over an area of several hundred yards—was a sight which the inhabitants of the region flocked to see. There was not a single wolf's bone among them, and this fact enables us to reconstruct the end of the scene. The lean, gray hunters must have stopped at the edge of the cliff to sniff at the empty space, perhaps detecting, in spite of the snow, the odor of the fantastic banquet which awaited them, and seeking at once the paths that would lead them to it.

In days when the herds roaming over the plains had no enemies other than wolves and Indians armed with lances or bows and arrows, the loss of fifty or a hundred thousand buffalo did not much matter. For one herd that was wiped out, a thousand survived. With their numbers reenforced by new births and reinvigorated by natural selection, the buffalo lived on through the intemperance of the changing seasons and all the other difficulties which Nature placed in their way. It seemed as if the species were destined to be immortal. Then one day, not far from a salty spring . . .

The little herd which had set up summer quarters in this grassy, shaded valley was leading a monotonously peaceful existence. The buffalo grazed and ruminated over a wide area. From time to time one or another of them would make his way to the stream, and several companions would follow. They drank deep of the salty water, preferring it to any other. Then they went back to their pasture.

When the migration period approached, bringing the urge to fall in with the great herd, they ceased grazing and took no nourishment whatsoever. But they continued to bathe and drink. On a day when they were wending their way to the river, a shot rang out and one of them fell dead. None of them had ever heard a gun. The buffalo walking immediately behind the one that had been killed was mildly surprised to stumble over his dead body. But, making his way around it, he went on toward the stream.

Knee-deep in the water, with their heavy heads hanging, the buffalo drank at their ease. From time to time a shot rang out, and on the shore another buffalo fell. But the rest went on walking. The buffalo were neither deaf nor blind; they heard the shots and saw their fellows fall to the ground, but between the two facts they established no connection.

This scene, repeated over and over, was to lead almost to the total extermination of the sixty or seventy million buffalo which originally inhabited North America. The first men to open fire upon them were Spaniards, armed with muskets, in the sixteenth century. But they barely scratched the surface. The great massacre began two centuries later.

The white men killed the buffalo for the profit from hides, meat, and even horns, which were made into combs and buttons. Most frequently they stole up on them in pasture and shot them down one after another. A few sportsmen chose to hunt them, as the Indians had done, when they were in the migration; but they were a distinct minority.

The Indians had never killed more than enough buffalo to

satisfy their immediate needs. At first the massacre revolted them. But, alas, they were fascinated by the weapons that spat thunder: the rifle and revolver. The first time that a white man said to an Indian, "Bring me so many buffalo and this gun is yours," the Indian accepted with alacrity. Sometimes the white man offered him alcohol—firewater; and, once an Indian had tasted this, he could not get along without it. The Indians who consented to supply the white men with game must have understood that the catastrophic extinction of the species was near at hand when they first saw white men shooting buffalo from ambush and then letting them rot without bothering so much as to cut out their tongues. These men were not professional hunters, but pioneers and ranchers who shot for the fun of it.

If this kind of fun seems to be both brutal and dull, it must be remembered that the pioneers, as a rule, did not come from social circles of great distinction. Many of them, in their old homes, would never have received a hunting permit. But in this new land they were not only permitted but practically obliged to use a gun. No one went unarmed into the wilderness, and the rifle was just as necessary a tool as the ax, the pick, and the shovel. There is no need to look further for the cause of the pioneers' passionate devotion to firearms. Their dream was to be armed with pearl-handled revolvers. And any child is eager to try out a new toy.

The white men could kill every last buffalo and still be sure of survival. But for the Indians, these animals were irreplaceable; the buffalo's extinction implied their own. The idea of hiring out as ranch laborers for the white men never crossed their minds. And so one evening when some settlers, anxious over friends who failed to return from the hunt, went to look they found them dead, minus the skin on top of their heads. In other words, scalped. The Indians had given the signal for war, war in defense of the buffalo.

October, 1867. Medicine Lodge, in southern Kansas, was still a typical western frontier town. But the streets were unusually bustling, and large numbers of wagon trains crowded the outskirts. In a flat area, not far away, there were two groups of tents, several hundred yards apart.

Over the nearer group waved the American flag. Here were four generals, three senators, and one cabinet member, who had come all the way from Washington. The tents of the other group, actually Indian tepees, were the headquarters of five Indian chiefs: Santanta, Kicking Bird, Black Kettle, Medicine Arrow, and Lone Wolf. Neither the government dignitaries nor the rough cowboys who thronged the saloons of Medicine Lodge saw anything funny about their names, such as we hear nowadays only on the lips of pink-cheeked cub scouts. In October, 1867, these names actually inspired fear. And it was to eliminate the fear that the federal government had called the Indian chiefs to a meeting. The white men wanted to keep their scalps, and the Indians were anxious to preserve the buffalo which played such a large part in their tribal existence. The hope was to come to a signed understanding.

Long before the hour for the meeting, the whole of Medicine Lodge crowded behind the line of soldiers stretched from one camp to the other. Every detail of the ceremony had been arranged with the Indians. The Indians must not be irritated, and yet the white men must not lose face before them. The Indians were to set out on horseback from their camp and to be met by the generals, on horseback also. Both parties would dismount at exactly the same time. Suddenly the Indian riders appeared in the open space before their tepees. As they rode forward a murmur rose among the crowd.

One thing must not be forgotten: none of the white men had ever seen Indian chiefs in ceremonial dress, in the many-colored, feathered attire which children's book illustrations and fancy-dress costumes have made so tediously familiar to us. To these white men an Indian was a copper-skinned savage, half naked or clothed in a rude pelt, perhaps with a single feather stuck into his hair—not to be compared with these brightly decked statues, borne solemnly across the green grass by horses that drew involuntary whistles of admiration. Before this sight met the view of the rough frontiersmen they had been uncertain about their own feelings. Should they yell, "Hurrah!" and hope for a peace treaty, or "Kill them!" remembering friends and comrades who had lost their lives? It gave them a queer sensation to see the redskins unpunished and surrounded with honor. Yes, they had had their doubts, but now the magnificence of the Indians' dress and the dignity of their bearing swept them into a mood of childlike wonder. The murmur which rippled through the crowd was indubitably one of admiration. As for the Indians, the ritual designs on their cheeks and foreheads could not have been more immobile had they been painted on faces of stone. These men, who could identify an animal prowling in the night by the way his footsteps made the leaves rustle, or pick out a bird flying across the sun, now seemed to hear and see nothing, indeed, to be conscious of nothing around them.

From the other camp the generals were advancing. The two groups halted at a distance of four paces, and none of the Indian statues came to life until at least one of the white leaders had slackened his reins and taken a foot out of its stirrup.

The generals found to their surprise that Medicine Arrow and his companions had learned to read a map. The treaty which they signed, after several days of palaver, stipulated that the Indians of this region should henceforth remain south of the Arkansas River and no white men should hunt buffalo there.

But no treaty can endure long when there is a clash between two vital necessities. Professional hunters had to kill ever increasing numbers of buffalo, because the market price was dropping lower and lower. When they could no longer make a sufficient kill north of the Arkansas, they crossed it. And the Indians, on their side, could not permit the slaughter of the animal so indispensable to their economy on territory which they had been led to believe would be respected. That is, not without condemning themselves to extermination. And so the war flared up again.

It is a curious fact that none of the makers of western movies based on the historic war between red men and white has brought out its tragically fateful motivation, in the form of a four-footed animal. If they had, their pictures might have some enduring human value instead of remaining almost without exception at a childish level, showing the Indians as a bunch of whooping scalp collectors. But perhaps people have preferred to maintain this convention.

Yet, at the time, many reasonable Americans found it utterly senseless for men, even if they were of two different races, to kill one another for the sake of an animal. The only way to put an end to such folly would have been to stop the buffalo's extermination. Organizations sprang into being, and many states instituted protective legislation. But one general repeated insistently: "Rubbish!"

The eminent zoologist Martin S. Garretson, historian and defender of the American buffalo and founding secretary of the American Bison Society, through whose efforts the last herds were finally saved, quotes the exact words of General Phil Sheridan, in command of the military department of the Southwest, who hastened to Austin, the capital of Texas, when he heard that this state was on the point of copying the conservation laws of Kansas and Colorado:

"Let them kill, skin and sell until the buffalo is extermi- nated, as it is the only way to bring about a lasting peace and allow civilization to advance."

Death to the buffalo! Death to the Indians! One is re- minded of the ancient Roman emperors, turning their thumbs down to dispose of a gladiator who had not taken their fancy. But before the buffalo disappeared, they were to furnish a new kind of popular sport, not unlike that which drew crowds to the Roman arena.

Alongside almost every western railway station, barnlike buildings were thrown up to serve as storehouses for the buffalo hides. These were jammed full, and often the incom- pletely cleaned hides stank to high heaven. But their stench did not dampen the enthusiasm of the frontiersmen who came to stare at posters announcing "buffalo hunt excur- sions." The railways had hit upon a new tourist attraction, a special train for buffalo hunters, along with ordinary sensa- tion seekers who welcomed a chance to witness the hunt. In various towns local hunters guided the visitors to the graz- ing herds. Usually the animals took to their heels and were shot down in flight, but occasionally a wounded or rebellious bull turned and charged his assailants. In this case, the pro-

fessionals took over, in order that no accident should spoil
the fun. The organization of excursions of this kind was a
booming business.

One of the most competent and energetic organizers was
General Sheridan. At a White House reception, where he
was introduced to Grand Duke Alexis, son of Czar Alexander
II of Russia, he had a magnificent idea.

"Your Highness must make a tour of the Far West!" he
exclaimed. "A buffalo hunt on the plains, there's an experience for you!"

The Grand Duke was reputed to be a fervent sportsman,
and he made no secret of the fact that his two favorite sounds
were those of a cracking rifle and the popping cork of a
champagne bottle. Amid festive toasts he agreed to the expedition. Sheridan telegraphed orders to set up a hunting
camp near North Platte, Nebraska, and commandeered a
regiment of cavalry, several infantry and supply units, and
a number of scouts who were in army service.

"What are those pointed tents over there?" the Grand
Duke asked as he got out of his special train.

"Indian tepees, Your Highness," said the general in charge
of the camp. "General Sheridan has brought in an entire
village—fifty braves with their wives and children."

Sheridan, emerging from another railway car, proposed a
round of champagne to baptize the camp. The atmosphere
was supremely gay. The Grand Duke himself, with only a
few followers, led the first "attack" against a herd which had
been located, most opportunely, only fifteen miles away. Captain Cody, alias Buffalo Bill, was responsible for the royal
guest's security. Everything went well, and, once the Grand
Duke had brought down the first buffalo, the hunt was declared open. The Russian was not convinced that an Indian

could kill a buffalo with a bow and arrow. And so Sheridan gave orders to round up one bull and drive him toward the camp.

"Two Lance will show Your Highness what he can do!"

Two Lance, a Sioux chief, was one of those submissive Indians who had comprehended that his people were hopelessly outmatched and the best they could hope to do was play a part in the palefaces' amusements. Melancholy and alcoholism had not yet ruined the Indians' physical abilities. Now, the chief's first arrow did the trick. It was so accurately aimed and shot with such power that it went straight through the buffalo's heart and stuck out through the opposite side.

"Amazing!" said the Grand Duke, and he gave Two Lance a twenty-dollar gold piece.

In two days of hunting the party killed fifteen hundred buffalo. On the evening of the second day an army telegram brought news that another herd had been located, one hundred thirty miles east of Denver. Sheridan proved his strategical skill. He sent out two special trains and an advance guard of cavalry from Fort Wallace, Kansas, to ready a second camp and to give his visitor the pleasure of a second hunt with hardly any deviation from his itinerary. The Grand Duke was duly grateful, and the souvenirs which he took back to Russia included twenty-five stuffed buffalo heads as well as a bow and quiver which had belonged to Two Lance.

The Grand Duke's name has been forgotten, but Buffalo Bill's is almost as famous as that of Napoleon. Even today his legend furnishes material for comic books and western pictures. Buffalo Bill early in his career was hired by the Kansas Pacific to supply buffalo meat to the railroad construction crews. Successively a champion buffalo hunter, an army scout, and a guide for the elaborate hunting parties, he realized

that the end of the great herds might also cut short his good
fortune. He proceeded to organize a circus, which traveled
all over the United States and even through Europe, and
whose main attraction was an imitation buffalo hunt. The
actors were tame, captive animals, descended from the survivors of the great massacre, and bought or rented from
zoological societies.

As for General Sheridan, he remained to the very end
a promoter of the large-scale circus operating on the great
plains. Not so very many years ago there were still Americans
who remembered the fabulous impression left on the West by
the "millionaires' hunt" organized by Sheridan in 1874. James
Gordon Bennett, publisher of the *New York Herald,* the
founder of the Western Union, and several other tycoons of
the day, along with some high-ranking army officers, took
part. One general wrote a sixty-eight-page pamphlet describing this hunt-to-end-all-hunts, including the menus of the
meals served to the participants. At dusk, after the last shot
had been fired, they returned wearily to camp. Hulking
buffalo bodies still lay scattered over the plain, waiting for
the butchers' wagons to carry them away. Meanwhile, in the
camp, smoke rose over the great fires where the meat was
roasting, soldiers set out decorated tables, and a band played.
Far away to the north, the survivors of the great herd, which
had been headed back and then pursued several times over,
trotted uninterruptedly, in parallel lines, through the deepen-
ing twilight. Had cruel awareness of the danger of the white
man at last penetrated those heavy heads, those craggy foreheads? Perhaps, but far too late.

The buffalo abandoned their normal migration routes and
took refuge in the north, beyond the Yellowstone River,
where there was still virgin land and no smell of gunpowder.

But civilization would not let them alone. In 1880, when the Northern Pacific Railway extended its track across the northern plains, hundreds of successors to Buffalo Bill opened fire on the refugee herds, which once more provided meat for the workers and extra profit from the sale of the hides. The buffalo was doomed to disappear. There was an element of fatality about it. The idea of extermination, fostered by the spectacular hunts described above, was now widespread among all segments of the population. People thought of killing buffalo as part of the march of civilization, like clearing and plowing the land.

In the autumn of 1883, ten thousand wild buffalo, the very last of their line, were haplessly wandering through North Dakota, and their exterminators used a new method against them.

The buffalo were covered with gray dust, as if they had not bathed for many days. They trotted, but slowly and jerkily. Many of them let their mouths sag and their tongues hang out. Obviously they had accomplished a long and difficult journey. It was near the end of October, and the weather was unusually warm and dry. Toward the close of day the buffalo fell into first a slow pace and then a walk. At last they halted, all together, but without bumping or confusion, as though at a signal. However, they did not lie down in the usual way, but continued to stand, moving occasionally from side to side as if in the expectation that something would happen. Meanwhile the night deepened. Suddenly a bellow rose from the edge of the herd, a deep, guttural complaint. The bull from which it came raised his head, slowly and almost painfully, toward the horizon. Some of his companions approached him and bellowed also, stretching out their muzzles in the same direction. These buffalo had detected the vicinity of water. Abruptly they began first to walk and then to trot, and the rest of the herd followed.

Under the starry sky the herd, in parallel lines, moved rapidly forward, the water drawing them like a magnet. There was a rise in the ground, but instead of slowing them it caused them to break into a gallop. The old or wounded veterans in the rear could not keep up and so they lagged behind, but no wolves were there to attack them. For some days, the wolves had dropped out of the picture. The herd galloped, then, across the rising plain, with dripping tongues hanging out of open mouths. The goal toward which they were so breathlessly striving was one of the few things that perhaps actually corresponded to an idea in their dense brains. Water, wonderful life-giving water, enough for them to drink their fill and then bathe their weary bodies.

The front line had reached the top of the rise and, impelled by its own momentum, had started to pour down the other side, when it halted in utter confusion and shied off to one side, as if it had run smack into a wall. The lines that followed did exactly the same, turning aside in disorder and dismay. There was indeed a wall, a hundred yards ahead, a wall of fire. At the bottom of the slopes lay the pond, some two hundred paces across, which the buffalo were seeking, ringed by flames. The flames rose from piles of burning branches, which were not continuous but were close enough together to prevent the buffalo from passing through. The men who had set them out had this in mind. The flames lit up their camp and their wagon trains, some fifty yards from the water. Over a large area, between the Moreau and Cannon Ball rivers, every spring, pond and river was shut off, all night long, by fire. This was the white man's new way of attacking the buffalo.

Any wild animal, whether or not he has ever seen fire before, instinctively recognizes it as a terrifying and invincible enemy. The herd galloped away, leaving both fire and water behind. Finally the animals slowed down to a walk and then halted. They were suffering more and more from thirst, and their recent fright had dazed them. But they had not gone far enough to lose the scent of the water. After a short time some of them bellowed and led a return in the direction of the pond. Perhaps they had forgotten the recent apparition of the flames. Almost certainly they had forgotten that for several nights now they had suffered the same traumatic experience. They were afflicted more and more grievously with thirst, and the magnetic power of the water acted more and more powerfully upon them.

Around the pond fires were still burning. The men had piled more branches upon them. And the herd, once more taking fright, wheeled around and fled in disorder. All night long the buffalo repeated this vicious circle, seeking the water and then fleeing the fire. And throughout the entire region, wherever there was a pond or spring or river, other herds exhausted themselves in the same way. The predatory wolves could not endure this senseless regime; when they found that they could not obtain water, they sought it somewhere else.

When it was sufficiently light, and the buffalo tried again to reach the water, the white men picked up their guns. It was not for pleasure that they had gathered wood and stayed up all night feeding the fires. It was impossible to kill buffalo at night, even in the glow of the flames. When day came they let the fires die out and carried out their projected operation.

The buffalo did not march deliberately toward the water, as if to satisfy a normal thirst; they threw themselves upon it. Those that managed to reach the pond without being shot enjoyed a few moments of grace. They plunged and drank deeply, indifferent to what was going on about them. The hunters preferred to kill them on dry land, so as to avoid hauling the bodies to the place where they were to be skinned. But even under the gunfire, the thirsty buffalo pressed forward. Wounded as they were, they dragged themselves all the way to the water and ceased struggling only when they had begun to drink, even though life and consciousness were fast ebbing away. Behind them, other wounded animals, unable to go so far, spasmodically shook their hulking bodies, while from the rear an onrushing crowd of their fellows trampled them down until they themselves fell. The relative silence which reigned between shots contrasted strangely with the violence of their movements. In their agony, the buffalo did nothing more than groan and sigh, so that the onlookers felt as if they were witnessing the massacre of a band of deaf mutes. Above the pond the first rays of the rising sun shone through an early morning mist with which mingled the smoke from the dying fires.

CHAPTER IV

THE EIGHTH PLAGUE

The Arabian sand was dry and sterile. The stars followed their courses in the sky, but nothing happened on the flat land below. The only indication of the passage of time was an almost imperceptible seasonal change in the appearance of the stunted bushes which sprouted here and there. In spring they were slightly less yellow and dusty than during the rest of the year. There was practically no rainfall, and so it was hard to see why. Probably they owed their new lease on life to a minute increase of the moisture in the air. From one end of the year to the other, all the rest of the landscape seemed utterly dead.

And yet this desert contained one other manifestation of life, infinitesimal in size and level with the ground. Periodically, groups of whitish worms dotted the sand. Each one of them shook itself and opened up, revealing a colorless but perfectly shaped creature only a quarter of an inch long, but provided with the head, body, feet, and general structure of an insect. For these were the larvae of a kind of locust known as *Schistocerca flaviventris*. After five minutes' exposure to the light they took on a vague gray-green color, disappeared in the bushes, and were not seen again.

The bushes served as both shelter and larder. Feeding upon

the yellow leaves, the larvae grew and became adult insects, with wings. The wings had little practical use, since the locusts hardly moved at all and spent most of their lives hidden in the bushes. When they attained sexual maturity, they mated and died. A short time after this, the new larvae which they had produced appeared on the sand, in a prelude to the same obscure, monotonous existence. The cycle was repeated, without change, several years in succession. Then one spring day, a few weeks after a rainfall, a quite incomprehensible event took place.

Whitish worms appeared here and there on the sand, and opened up, revealing themselves as tiny, colorless creatures a quarter of an inch long. The larvae remained motionless on the ground until, after five minutes' exposure to light, they acquired a tegument or protective shell structure and took on a vague gray-green color. Two minutes after this, quite incomprehensibly, their hereditary color turned to a dark brown. A minute later it was almost black. The larvae shook themselves, but they did not seek shelter in the bushes like their predecessors. They moved toward one another until they were all in one place. *Schistocerca flaviventris* had entered into a new phase and become *Schistocerca gregaria*.

During the second half of September 1954, telephone calls to the British Anti-Locust Research Center and to the French Committee for the Study of the Biology of Acridians and National Anti-Acridian Bureau were unusually frequent. The calls came from correspondents of the Service for the Protection of Vegetation in North Africa, who wanted to know if there was any reason for alarm. A few days earlier, bulletins had informed them of an abnormal abundance, in several African localities, of larvae of the *Schistocerca gregaria*, or migratory locust. The area between the mountains of Tibesti and Ennedi in French Equatorial Africa seemed to be particularly infested. Wasn't there danger that a swarm of adult locusts might descend from these parts into the cultivated regions? During the winter of 1953–1954 Morocco had been invaded in this manner.

"It is impossible to predict with any certainty," was the reply. "But we have reason to believe that ever since the autumn of 1948 a cycle of invasions has been under way. At this time exceptionally heavy rains fell on the deserts of eastern Arabia. These created unusually favorable conditions for the development of ordinary locusts, and their abundance provoked the transformation into locusts of the gregarious and migratory kind, which proceeded to spread out in every direction. After this there came alternate periods of activity and quiescence. Even now, the superabundant larvae may encounter conditions unfavorable to their further growth and perish. The French Equatorial African Agricultural Bureau has already started to combat the locusts on the ground and is prepared to deal with them in the air. We will keep you informed of further developments, so that you may take any necessary defense measures against invasion."

On the Arabian desert the larvae had begun their lives with amazing energy, by moving toward one another. And yet on the very day of their birth, when the sun set, their vitality suddenly weakened so that by dusk it seemed as if they must inevitably perish. They stayed in one place, incapable of movement, and a single gust of wind swept thousands of them away. Finally night fell.

But the next day, as soon as the first slanting rays of the sun struck the ground, the larvae came back to life and shook themselves again. The wind had scattered them over an expanse of desert positively enormous in proportion to their size. Once more they moved toward one another. They assembled not in a single mass, but in a number of huge patches. Seen from close by, these assemblies had none of the characteristics of a disorderly crowd. Every one of them was like a regiment, trained to maneuver in perfect unison. No officer stood out in front to give commands, and yet each individual soldier imitated exactly the slightest move of his neighbor.

Already the larvae were on the march. Their regiments moved in different directions over the ground. Some invisible general must have watched over their maneuvers and sent out orders, for from time to time two regiments which had come close together merged into one and advanced with increasing determination, in the direction which had been followed by the larger grouping before. Other regiments were attracted by this purposefulness and joined the same line of march. By the end of the day, the division had swollen to the size of an army corps.

Meanwhile new written and telephonic information continued to pour into the anti-locust bureaus. By the beginning of autumn the situation could be summarized in the following report:

"Abnormally large bands of wingless locusts have been reported in the Anglo-Egyptian Sudan, to the northeast, east, and southeast of Lake Chad, in Eritrea, and at various points in the region between Lake Chad and Mauritania. Efforts to combat these bands have been handicapped by the difficulty of locating them on the ground. They are rarely visible from the air and motorized ground searchers cannot prospect at random. The first alarm is given by the local population. As soon as a Center has been alerted, vehicles go out to spray hexachlorocyclohexane powder. The natives have methods of their own: they take sticks and push the larvae into bags, in which they are later crushed, or else into trenches filled with burning gasoline. But many bands, coming from the desert, are discovered only in close proximity to inhabited places, after they have already caused considerable damage to both large- and small-scale cultivation. Wingless locusts are remarkably active and voracious, and few natural obstacles can stop them; they swim across rivers in spite of the fact that the current carries thousands of them away. There is still hope that unfavorable weather conditions and heavy rains may halt their progress or even destroy them. Their very number makes them an object of attack by birds of prey. Nevertheless they constitute a serious threat. Our network of watchers is functioning in perfect order. Planes and cars are out scouting, so that the first flights of winged insects to leave the ground may be immediately discovered and attacked."

Meanwhile the armies of wingless locusts were proceeding nine to twelve miles a day, resting every night and getting under way again in the morning. As they moved along they underwent a spectacular change of color.

The larvae had left their first envelope fully equipped except for wings. Soon rapid growth made the rigid external armor which constituted their bony structure too narrow, and they split it down the middle and cast it aside. Their soft body was then extremely vulnerable, but within a few hours they were protected by another stiff, pigmented envelope, which lasted until the next time they had a sudden access of growth. Five times they shed, and each time donned an

armor of a different color: near-black, whitish with yellow
spots, green, and bright pink. They did not take on their
definitive yellow until they attained sexual maturity, that is,
near the end of their life. After the fourth shedding their
wings started to grow. None of these transformations affected
to any noticeable extent their speed. Millions of armies of a
varying pink color progressed in different directions across
Africa, some of them along a front as much as six miles long.

The last shedding, which permitted full development of
the wings, was longer and more complex than the rest. Every
insect hung, head down, from the twig or branch of a bush
and worked hard to free itself from the enclosing envelope,
which finally peeled off like a glove. The long wings, covered
by sheaths and extending beyond the length of the body,
were at first like a pair of cumbersome, flabby arms. But
soon, in the light of day, they acquired a tegument, or protective shell structure.

One morning, under the warm sun, the locusts felt able
to spread and stretch their wings. They began to shake them
hesitantly at first and then faster and faster. Without any
apparent consultation, they had lined up facing the same
direction, like airplanes on a carrier. A few insects made their
wings vibrate very vigorously and then took off from the
ground. They rose high, describing circles in the air. This
sight galvanized those still on the ground, and more and more
miniature planes rose to form squadrons in the air. The
squadrons flew close together, producing a characteristic
rattle like that of a drum. Without pause, increasing numbers
joined the flight. So it was that the great army which for
days had marched invincibly across the ground was transformed into a cloud, inspired by the same single-minded
will. It looked like an aerial river, a thick pink ribbon, rising

and expanding, then closing ranks in an undulating motion, like a sheet flapping in the breeze. An incessant drumming sound, like that of hail, accompanied it all the way. Now the cloud ceased to weave circles in the air. The shadow it traced on the sand was moving in a resolutely straight direction.

Africa is a continent of immense spaces. The cloud of Arabian locusts traveled hundreds of miles, stopping at night and setting out again in the morning. Now it flew at altitudes of six to nine hundred feet; now it rose to three or four thousand feet and looked like a wisp of smoke against the blue sky. Storks with beaks clacking attacked it in full flight, kites and other birds fell upon it, decimating its numbers; but the cloud pursued its way.

Little by little it had changed color, from rose to yellow; and again it prepared to alight. Expanding, compressing, fluctuating in the breeze, it lost altitude; and as it glided toward the ground the drumming sound became louder and louder. Of a sudden this died completely away, and there was a cloud no more. The locusts were imperceptible against the sand, and the only sign of their presence was a strange tremor of the ground, such as to give any witness an eery feeling.

Nothing grew in this desolate place except a little brush and cactus of the kind amid which the locusts had been born. If their hundreds of thousands of powerful jaws had started to function, a few minutes would have seen the end of this miserable vegetation. At other resting places along the way they had accomplished such total destruction. But the present landing was not for the purpose of obtaining food. The locusts were animated by quite a different desire.

The adult *Schistocerca gregaria,* at close range, resembles a dragon in miniature. If by some Alice-in-Wonderland magic man were reduced in size and the locust were magnified, proportionately to their relative numbers on the globe, the result would fill man with terror. Even without that magic, the locust's measurements are astounding. With wings outspread it has a span of five inches; with wings folded three inches. But its most chilling aspect is its metallic nudity. This insect, which preceded man on earth by several thousand years, seems to have passed beyond the stage of flesh and blood, of the normal organic life which we share with the mammals, the birds, and even the fish, and to have evolved into a kind of robot, pregnant with terror. The locust's rigid wings are machinelike; its disproportionate thighs are like steel springs. All its movements are dry, jerky, mechanical.

Schistocerca gregaria is the locust of the Bible, without any doubt whatsover. It is recognizable in the frescoes of Egyptian tombs as early as 2500 B.C. The book of Joel describes its behavior in a highly symbolical style but also with scientific precision: "The appearence of them is as the appearance of horses." The prophet is quite right, but the head is that of an iron horse. Hold a blade of grass out to Schistocerca, and the eighteen components of its jaws go immediately into action, lubricated by a brown saliva which looks like motor oil. The horse's head emerges from a rigid armored hood; the eyes are protruding portholes; the short antennae belong to a two-way radio station. A human spectator can see the reaction to any message they send out, but does not hear its transmission.

The females in the cloud that had come down to earth were more numerous and more voluminous than the males; that they were heavier too was evident from the way they moved over the ground. Each of them bore a burden of eggs and the spryer males drew near to fecundate them. The robotlike suitors did not necessarily approach the nearest females. They began by moving first in one direction and then in another, as if their mechanism were out of order. Perhaps thousands of messages were crisscrossing on the expanse of sterile sand. When a male finally stopped in front of the female of his choice he addressed her by vibrating his posterior femurs. Many species of locust and grasshopper execute a love song by rubbing their armored thighs against their wing sheaths. Schistocerca's vibration could not be heard by the human ear, but it was most certainly audible to the female. This tête-à-tête lasted varying lengths of time, in some cases several hours. Then in each case the male went around and around the female —somewhat awkwardly, for he could fly or jump more easily than he could walk. Finally he straddled her, in the act of fecundation.

For all its rigid exterior, the locust's underbelly consists of rings that make it as flexible as a garden hose. Each straddling male bent his abdomen in such a way as to fit around that of the female and allow the two copulative organs to meet. A human observer could not have failed to be surprised by the grace and ingenuity of the movement. And he would have been touched by the way the male fluttered his wings. This flutter was biologically unnecessary and betrayed a humble joy. It proved that at this crowning moment of the locust's life, when he participated in the great act of creation, he was not a perfectly adapted and predetermined mechanism. No robot will ever have the power to quiver in this way!

Hundreds of thousands, indeed millions, of fecundated eggs were buried in the sand by a large-scale boring operation. Every female steadied herself on the sand, stiffened her stomach, and drove her telescopic extremity, equipped for boring, down to a depth of four inches. The male stood by, encouraging her in the work. While all the females were thus occupied they secreted a foamy substance for gluing the grains of sand together into an impermeable cylinder; and in it they laid their eggs. Covering it with a lid of mucus, they withdrew their telescopic part. They laid fifty to a hundred eggs at once, as large as grains of rye, and did this five or six times. Then, totally exhausted, they died. The males, without apparent reason for exhaustion, died a short time after. To the species their usefulness was over.

Days and nights went by. The millions of eggs deposited by the cloud out of Arabia lay in the sand four inches under the surface where their parents' bodies had rotted, dried, and finally blown away. After three or four weeks they broke open, releasing tiny pale worms. At the bottom of the holes drilled by the female locusts, each collection of larvae was like a group of children imprisoned in a well with a heavy iron cover. Moreover, each larva was swaddled in a ghostly sheet, a membrane which remained around his body when it emerged from the egg. Yet these tiny creatures must have had some awareness of the exterior world, for they twisted and writhed in an effort to move upward, never downward. Their ascent did not cease until they came in contact with the cover that sealed the top of the cylinder.

Inside the enveloping membrane, every larva was completely formed, with not a single organ missing. The larvae differed from human babies in this important respect: they knew exactly what they had to do and did it, without tears or fuss. All together they pressed their necks against the hardened mucus cover. They contracted the ludicrously feeble muscles of their abdomens, and this contraction caused a bloody rupture on their necks, a frail vesicle, painful to see, but the first tool with which Nature equips the locust for its life struggle. The lid was solid and was tightly fitted, so that the larvae had to contract their muscles like so many wreslers at a county fair. But eventually they attained their aim. Once the lid was raised, the larvae scaled the walls of the well. As soon as they reached the ground they tore open the enveloping membranes and emerged, first whitish and then gray-green, into the light of the sun. A second later they changed color again and moved toward one another, just as their parents had done before them.

The swarm of locusts born in the Arabian desert was no more, but it had left descendants. Soon they too would be an army on the march and then a cloud in the air. On the immense deserts of Africa, the multiplication which had started in Arabia a few years before continued, generation after generation. Other armies marched, and other clouds flew.

In A.D. 125 the famine which followed upon the locusts' depredations in the Roman provinces of Cyrenaica and Numidia cost the lives of 200,000 people. Between 1925 and 1955, the same insects caused damage amounting to a billion dollars.

Locusts belong to the family of Acridiidae in the order of Orthoptera. They differ from grasshoppers (Orthoptera of a different family) in shorter antennae and other particulars, one of which causes them to be regarded with particular terror: they are strict vegetarians.

For thousands of years people believed that the destructive locusts belonged to an entirely separate species from that of the timid, differently colored variety, which lives hidden in shrubs and bushes. Then, around 1920, a Russian naturalist named Uvarov, who was studying two kinds of locust—one sedentary, *Locusta danica,* and the other migratory, *Locusta migratoria*—which differ not only in behavior but in color and certain anatomical details as well, declared that they were one and the same insect, subject, under certain circumstances, to a change, either in itself or in its descendants.

Several species of locusts undergo these mysterious transformations, known as "phases." Rémy Chauvin, a French scientist, has made a special study of Schistocerca, the locust of the Bible. Here are the phenomena which his laboratory studies have revealed.

A "sedentary-solitary" locust, *Schistocerca flaviventris,* of a pale green color, was placed in a glass jar with several "gregarious-migratory" (*Schistocerca gregaria*) brothers. In the course of a few hours he became yellow, like them, and changed even his disposition. Originally calm and sober, he became restless and voracious.

If male and female "solitary" locusts are put together their offspring, from the moment of birth, present all the characteristics of the "migratory" kind. The generation resulting from union of these offspring revert to the characteristics of the grandparents. But after two or three sheddings they turn again to the "migratory" form.

Scientists attribute the transformation to "group influence." Because we know how the psychology of a crowd differs from that of an individual, it is easy enough to believe that an animal's psychology and behavior may be modified in the course of cohabitation with his fellows. But the idea of a change in his anatomy—the migratory locusts have longer wings and a greater curve in the neck—strikes us as strange and almost terrifying.

Experiments prove that perception by the sedentary locust

of his companions' movements through the antennae determines his transformation. The process is at many points obscure, but it seems to be caused by a modification of the neuroendocrine balance. Here is considerable food for thought. Pavlov's work on conditioned reflexes has shown that, in man and the higher animals, the emotion caused by a single gesture, word, or sound may provoke glandular changes and hence organic lesions. These insects, in some ways so like robots, seem to be affected, under no greater stimulus, to the point of transformation not alone of their glandular secretions but of their whole anatomy.

Of course a glass jar has little in common with an Asian or African desert. Laboratory experiments cannot reproduce exactly what happens among insects in their natural environment, but they help us to understand it. As this chapter points out, locusts in the sedentary phase, *Schistocerca flaviventris*, are scattered over large areas, where they remain peacefully, generation after generation. Then a generation is born that acts differently from its predecessor and is gregarious-migratory. This transformation does not occur just anywhere. It has been observed that there are definite favorable zones, one being in eastern Arabia, another in Madagascar, and probably a third in Mauritania.

If we knew exactly why these zones are favorable, the war against the locust could be conducted much more efficaciously. But, geographically and climatically, they are hard to distinguish from areas where the locusts remain sedentary. Apparently certain years differ subtly from the others in a way that increases the birthrate. And when the larvae are crowded more closely together, they become gregarious, like the ones in the glass jar. This is the story, in slightly simplified form. The locusts do not necessarily change character in a single generation. The species may pass through a transitional phase, and reach the migratory stage only in the generation that follows.

Let us add that, in the course of several generations, migratory locusts may return to a sedentary form. This happens when they encounter great storms inopportunely, or when, in the course of migration, they are decimated by the attacks of their natural enemies or of man. The remnants of their armies then appear to be demoralized; they slow down, halt, and finally scatter. Their behavior alters, and they slip into the transitional phase and then become solitary. But regressions of this kind are unusual. More often, the migratory adventure continues.

The plane had taken off from the Center at four-thirty P.M.: a Fieseler Morane, equipped for observation and carrying in a bin one hundred thirty pounds of acricide. It was twenty-six hundred feet above the expanse of savanna. About five o'clock, the observer said to his companion:

"Thirty degrees to the left. I think I see something."

Three minutes later there was no doubt as to what he had seen. And within three minutes more, the plane was directly above the object of its search. The late afternoon sun shone on a cloud of locusts about a thousand feet above the ground. The pinkness of the cloud indicated that the locusts had undergone their last shedding and were about to turn yellow with the achievement of sexual maturity. The cloud must have been three miles long and half a mile wide; it proceeded with an undulating motion like that of a piece of drapery flapping in the breeze, alternately expanding and compressing, and accompanied by the dark shadow which it cast to the right of it, on the ground. Its speed was approximately eighteen miles an hour.

The plane, traveling considerably faster, soon left the cloud behind. The pilot tipped the wings and swung it around. Once more, the pink cloud was directly below. It was impractical to spray acricide upon the locusts in flight. The operation would have been too imprecise, even from close above. There was a risk of the locusts' rising into the plane's course, enveloping the motor and blocking its vents. Now the observer was taking the bearings of the cloud. He could be sure that there would be no change of direction. The locusts had settled upon their migratory course, and nothing could cause them to deviate from it.

The Morane circled over the cloud. Apparently the roar did not in the least disturb the millions of tiny flying machines below.

"Have you got it?" asked the pilot.

"Yes. All set."

The plane dipped its wings again and made for the Center from which it had started. The pink cloud appeared to shrink as it was left behind.

The two four-wheel-traction Dodges were parked side by side in front of the small cement buildings at the end of the landing strip. The team leader and the director of the Center looked at the Morane, which was rolling jerkily toward them.

"They must have found one," said the director, "or they wouldn't have come back so soon."

The plane stopped, the cabin door opened, and the observer jumped out, with a paper in his hand.

"Everything's in good order," he reported. "We left a

swarm some thirty-five miles away. You'll be able to reach it before dark."

The pilot joined them, and all four went inside to examine the map. The room was furnished with camp cots, two wardrobes, two pine tables and a two-way radio set-up.

"Give us some beer," said the director to the black boy.

The observer laid a protractor on the large map, pinned to one of the tables. He traced a pencil line and then calculated the distances with the aid of a compass.

"In two hours the swarm will be here," he said to the team leader, who was leaning over his shoulder. "In three hours it will be there. Under normal conditions, this is where it will alight. Does that suit you?"

"Perfect!" said the leader. "There are three villages near by, so we should find plenty of men to help us. We'll be off right away."

"Finish your beer," said the director, "even if it's warm. I'm still waiting for the kerosene-burning icebox. I know the money for it has been allotted."

The team leader opened a drawer and took out a compass, a pair of field glasses, and a folding map.

"Tell the crews we're getting ready to start," he said to the boy. And as he finished his beer he said questioningly to the airman: "Pink cloud?"

"Yes," said the pilot. "Beautiful color."

"Those bugs will eat themselves sick if they ever reach a place where anything grows. Here's hoping we nab them."

When he stepped out the native helpers were sitting in the two cars, and the motors were humming.

"Let's go—toward Dioura."

The cars had left the road and were moving fifteen miles an hour over the uneven, sandy ground, dotted with cacti and stunted bushes. The team leader, with the open map on his knees and the compass on the seat beside him, was looking straight ahead, through his field glasses. To the left, the sun was sinking toward the horizon, and behind the cars there rose a great cloud of dust. One could feel the heat of the powerful motors. Every now and then the leader would look at his map and then at his watch. He did not make any comment, but his face betrayed anxiety.

A voice called out from the other Dodge. One of the natives was standing up in the car and pointing to the right.

The team leader shifted his field glasses to look in that direction.

"O.K.!" he exclaimed. "We've got them! Good for you, Koumalo!"

The black with his keen eyes had been quicker than the European with the field glasses. This was not the first time. And Koumalo's ears were equally keen; he always heard the approach of a plane before anyone else. Meanwhile the cars had veered to the right.

"The swarm is flying at about three hundred feet," said the leader, still peering through his field glasses. "Drive due north. That's it. We must intercept it."

Less than a quarter of an hour later, the occupants of the cars glimpsed a sight that never failed to impress them. The rays of the sun, by this time nearly horizontal, lit the undulating sheet, which now had a shrimp-pink color, from below. The cars were moving parallel with the locusts, at the same speed, three hundred yards away. The hum of their motors drowned out that of the swarm.

"Don't drive too close, Dubula," said the leader. "If they were to swing over in our direction as they landed, we'd be in a pretty mess."

But the flying army did not deviate an inch from its straight line. It expanded and closed ranks, undulating all the while and heading steadily in the same direction.

"They're coming down!" called out one of the blacks.

The front part of the swarm was, indeed, approaching the ground, with the rest following obliquely after. But when it reached a certain level, the swarm straightened out and continued to fly. The cars continued along the same parallel line, weaving their way among clumps of bushes and hillocks of sand.

"If it were just a little cooler, they'd have come down by now," said the team leader. "Anyhow—"

He broke off, and all the blacks cried out together. The downward movement initiated by the front part of the swarm was transmitted like a giant wave all the way back. Sixty feet, thirty, fifteen . . . Hundreds of thousands of locusts hit the ground.

"Up and at them!" called the leader.

The two vehicles turned and made for the locusts, at full speed.

"Stop!"

The leader's car came to a grinding halt, followed by the other, and both drivers turned off the ignition. In the sudden silence they could hear the drumming, hail-like effect of the locusts' landing. A wide area, under the rays of the dying sun, was transformed before their eyes. The sheet, which now seemed bright red, covered the ground as far as they could see. Cacti and bushes had a ghostly air, covered with a solid mass of insects, crawling over one another. The drumbeat had ceased, and the only sound was a rustle, which rose from the all-enveloping carpet. The spectacle was fascinating and uncomfortable at the same time.

"Kumbi, the radio," said the leader. "Call the Center."

The airplane observer had been entirely right. There was a village less than two miles from the place where the locusts had landed. It was not even dark when the cars returned from it, jammed with blacks. Soon other volunteers ran up with branches. The locusts were spread over as much as twelve hundred acres, and clubbing them to death was out of the question. The first thing to do was to stake out the area so that it could be distinguished from the air. Soon, under the direction of the native assistants from the Center, regularly spaced fires were set all around. These were kept burning all night. The natives made repeated trips to the village, bringing back more branches for the fires. Their dark silhouettes moved to and fro among the lights and then melted away into the night. And all the while they called out to one another, laughed and even sang. The battle against the locusts was a welcome novelty and at the same time a kind of holy war.

During the second half of the night the team leader gave orders to bring leaves, grass and big cans of water. Toward the east, the sky turned white and then pink, paling the gleam of the fires. Leaves and grass, lightly sprinkled with water, were thrown onto the flames, and soon the area covered by the locusts was marked by smoke columns which indicated also to an airplane pilot direction and strength of the wind. The wind was feeble, so that the columns rose almost vertically. Conditions were extremely propitious.

Far away to the south the monoplane appeared in the pink sky. The sound of its motor grew gradually louder, and it increased in size. The natives shouted and gesticulated when they saw it turn directly over the area where the still torpid locusts covered the ground. The sun had not yet come up.

The plane flew on, then turned and came back, losing altitude until it was scarcely thirty feet above the carpet of locusts. From this point it attacked them with its spray of acricide, in a thick white cloud that trailed behind it and sank lower and lower, spreading over a wide surface, as the plane climbed again.

The Morane gained altitude, then turned around and swooped down to spray the locusts again. After several such descents the whole army was thoroughly covered. The team leader's assistants spread two pieces of white cloth in the shape of a cross on the ground near the cars. To the pilot, this familiar signal meant: "Spraying operation successfully completed."

The sun had risen and was sending its oblique rays over millions of locusts whose nerve centers must have been well on the way to paralysis.

But some of the locusts were not dead. The acricide had not touched all of them; besides, its full effect would not be felt for several hours. By eight o'clock the sun was warm enough to revive the insects that had escaped, and more and more of them left the ground to gather in a whirling swarm. Others, animated by the gregarious instinct, shook off the powder and rose to join them. Once more, a great sheet flapped in the air. After a few minutes it became clear that no more victims could leave the ground, and the migrants fell into close formation, rose to a height of about 700 feet and continued in the same direction as before, due north.

The men at the Centers knew that something like this was bound to happen. In order to wipe out all the locusts at once, they would have had to keep them longer on the ground, so that the acricide could complete its action. But the migrants never came to rest before night, and it was impossible to spray them before dawn. Actually, the operation which we have just described took place under the most favorable possible conditions. Often the swarm was located too late for the cars to overtake it before dusk. Or else a high wind scattered the spray.

The swarm whose partial destruction we have described was located again by the same Morane, late in the afternoon. Its point of departure, speed, and direction all were known, and so the plane overtook it almost exactly at the point calculated by the observer. Now the swarm was only half as large as before. The plane reported its probable landing place, and the two vehicles were on the spot before dark. Again a village was close by, and the spraying operation was conducted under equally favorable conditions.

Millions of locusts died. Over the sprayed area their rotting bodies produced a fearful smell. But the blacks felt no disgust and indeed had a certain satisfaction, because the corpses were those of their mortal enemies. Soon enough the hot sun burned away the charnelhouse odor.

Even this hecatomb had its survivors, and the smaller groups continued to fly northward. The third attack was carried out by another Center, notified by radio of its probable location. When the plane came upon the cloud of insects it was flying barely sixty-five feet above the ground. Probably the repeatedly poisoned locusts could not rise any higher, and they landed unusually early. The spray to which they were subjected the next morning was thoroughly ravaging.

This time the locusts covered with acricide did not awaken, but toppled over to one side and gave up the ghost. Others seemed to be aroused by the first rays of the sun; they were

moved by the irresistible impulse to resume flight and
dragged themselves into parallel lines, but could not spread
their wings. These hung pitifully at their sides, like long,
dead arms. For a few seconds they shook themselves con-
vulsively; then they too toppled over. Their great adventure
was complete. Never would they put on the definitive yellow
color of the mating season. Never would they approach a
female of the species and know the only joy of their gregarious and migratory existence.

Millions of locusts had been destroyed. But in that autumn
of 1954 messages and telephone calls continued to pour into
the Centers. Swarms were reported to be approaching from
Mauritania, the loop of the Niger River, the Sudan, and East
Africa.

The routes followed by the migratory locust stand out on
the map of Africa and southwest Asia like a number of widely
divergent arrows. The migrants do not always leave a barren
region for one that is agriculturally wealthy; they fan out
from their birthplaces to all four corners of the globe. But,
once a swarm has started in a given direction, it keeps to its
chosen path. And the messages which poured into the Centers made it appear that several arrows directed from Arabia
first toward the Sudan, Nigeria, and Mauritania were now
converging upon the northern lands of Algeria and Morocco.

The locust swarms were attacked on the ground by planes,
and also by jeeps when they alighted close enough to a
Center for these to reach them before their early-morning
departure from the ground. Some teams were alerted in time
to lay a mixture of bran and acricide along their route. Many
locusts attracted by this bait died as a result of their own
greed.

In one part of Africa a helicopter attacked a cloud of migrating locusts, in an attempt to alter its course. The machine, with its low speed and its capacity to remain motionless in the air, was able to follow the migrants at close range. Moreover, the ventilation produced by its rotor allowed it to penetrate the mass of locusts without any risk of their blocking its vents. The cloud attacked upon this occasion was a mile long and a quarter of a mile wide. The helicopter passed several times directly in front of it, spraying the air in such a way that the front-line locusts had to run straight into the lethal powder. A large number fell to the ground, but the others took their place and flew straight on, without swerving a single degree from their northward course, in the direction of a highly cultivated area.

However, there was reason to hope that man's effort would not be vain. This was not the first time that migratory locusts had invaded North Africa. Upon previous occasions their assault battalions either had been destroyed, one after another, or else had been reduced so far that a catastrophic mass invasion was no longer possible. Along with the messages of alarm, there were victory bulletins so numerous as to make it seem that all was well. At one point apparently the locusts had no chance at all of catching the defenders napping. Thousands of farmers and landowners in Algeria and Morocco sighed with relief.

But toward the end of October, 1954, airplanes and meteorological services announced that violent east-west winds were beginning to sweep over the entire continent. Their velocity increased hour by hour, and soon the whole area between the Sudan and the Atlantic Ocean was one vast storm.

No human eye could follow the spectacle that was evolving in the midst of this air mass, at varying altitudes; but fragmentary information from different places, notably from the western coast, give us an idea. All locusts old enough to fly were blown from east to west. The storm drove great clouds of them, like so many paper kites, toward the Atlantic Ocean. Every time a cloud catapulted into the water, millions of insects perished. It was as if a giant ventilator were sweeping the land clear of the plague which had for so long besieged it. For twenty-four hours this was the general impression.

In the evening of October 31, the meteorological services announced: "The storm is changing direction. Within a few hours it will be blowing from south to north." Early in the morning of November 1, ships in the vicinity of the Canary Islands still reported clouds of locusts so broad and thick that they sometimes darkened the sky. Most of them went over the islands and perished in the sea.

These were the last victims of the movement from east to west. But the locusts that were still above land when the storm veered to the north were now carried from the western Sahara to the Anti-Atlas Mountains. On rising air currents, they managed somehow to cross the mountains, although later millions of frozen bodies were found in the snow. But this loss was negligible, for some of the clouds were as large as ninety square miles.

Once this range was crossed, the locusts faced another and more formidable barrier, the Atlas Mountains. Although the wind was diminishing it was still strong. They were whirled in a series of cross currents, before they finally floated down over the fertile valley of the Sous below.

Since the approach of night columns of stinking smoke had been rising from the ground, swept over the fields by the strong wind. Colonials and natives alike were burning old rubber tires and pots of tar in the hope of discouraging the locusts and persuading them to land somewhere else, in case the planes and cars sent out against them failed in their mission. Long before dawn the lights of these fires were sprinkled all over the countryside.

Now the sun was shining, and there was no presage of any dire event in the blue sky. It was hard to place any faith in the messages of alarm. Many of the colonials, and even the natives, had never seen a swarm of locusts. The invasion of the preceding year had been sporadic, leaving many localities untouched.

At ten o'clock a motorcyclist stopped in the main square. At once the villagers gathered around.

"Unless we're unexpectedly lucky," he said, "they're making straight for us."

He had seen the great red cloud with his own eyes. Ever since dawn planes, in relays, had followed it, traveling barely a thousand feet over the ground. And he had met soldiers in a jeep, from Tafellount, where the locusts had alighted the night before. Fields, orange groves, and roads had turned red, and automobiles had had to give way while the insects landed.

"What's going on?" one villager asked. "Aren't any precautions being taken?"

The motorcyclist shrugged his shoulders.

"They're doing all they can. As soon as the locusts land, planes and cars will come to sprinkle them. But by that time the damage will be done. It's like trying to empty the ocean with a sieve."

The whole day was one of anxiety, in varying degrees. In all probability, the locusts would not land before dusk, and if so it was to be hoped that the cloud would pass over to the north and devastate other men's land. This was not an altruistic point of view, but no one could fail to understand it. When bombs are falling, every solid citizen hopes to see them hit someone else's house rather than his own.

For a while, every hour that went by was a new cause for concern. Paradoxically enough, everyone longed to see the cloud appear. But the sky remained empty, and eyes ached from staring. Eventually the time came when this hope was reversed, and everyone hoped that the locusts would be delayed and land somewhere to the south, even if it were only four or five miles away. Still the sky was empty, and when the sun set, people were still standing around the square. The sun hung low in the west when a child called out:

"There's a plane!"

He waved his arm toward the south, and a man raised a pair of field glasses in the same direction.

"Two planes," he observed.

Indeed, two minute, shining points grew larger and larger, until they stood distinctly apart. They were making straight for the village, and it was easy to detect their motors' hum. Then they veered to the right, and the hum diminished and died away.

For a couple of minutes there was complete silence. The man with the field glasses continued to peer through them. He was a tall, well built fellow, obviously a colonial and a landowner. Two veins stood out on his neck. Suddenly he lowered the glasses, and two red circles marked where he had held them to his eyes. The rest of his face was deathly white, like that of a drowning man. He held the glasses at arm's length, pointing toward the south, as the child had done a few minutes before. Twice he opened and shut his mouth without saying a word. But there was no need to speak; everyone understood what he wanted to say.

A few seconds later the cloud was visible to the naked eye. In the distance it had a dark color. Actually, it was not distinctly outlined, alone in the middle of the sky, as many people had imagined. Rather, it was a cloak, which covered a large area toward the south and west. With sunset still two hours away, the cloud loomed ever larger on the horizon, apparently covering more and more of the sky. Under the oblique rays of the setting sun it became increasingly rosy.

No one knew the exact speed at which the insects were flying: nine to twelve miles an hour, perhaps faster if the wind was behind them. But the columns of smoke which continued to rise over the fields indicated that the wind was diminishing in intensity. Many of the men who stood petrified in the square must have been making mental calculations, clinging to the hope that the cloud would blow over. But most of them were pessimistic. The spectacle was too grandiose and terrible to end in any but a dramatic manner. The end-of-the-world feeling that stabbed at their hearts could not be based on mere illusion.

The men who had this feeling were not mistaken. Under normal conditions the cloud might have gone over the village before dusk and landed farther north. But the tens of millions of locusts now darkening a whole segment of sky had made an abnormally long and hard journey. The wind had carried them over the Ahaggar and the Anti-Atlas Mountains; they were hungry and exhausted, and the cultivated fields and orange groves immediately below seemed like the Promised Land.

A large number of natives, emerging from God knows where, ran through the fields waving rags of cloth and uttering hoarse cries. The shadow of the locust cloud was traveling toward them, and they were running to meet it. Already the sky was red above them. The cloud began to descend. From the village square the undulation of its upper surface, extending endlessly into the distance, could be seen distinctly. And the terrible rattling sound of millions of tiny drums, a sound so dense that it sounded at times like a whistle, filled the air.

The eclipsing shadow came on, steadily widening. Horses grazing in a field whinnied and galloped away; cows mooed, and dogs ran across the square. The red cloud continued to descend, crushing the columns of smoke below it. The hail of drumbeats was deafening and everyone had vacated the square. People had gone indoors and hastily shut their doors and windows. But the cloud did not come all the way to the village; it landed several hundred yards to the south, covering the ground with an endless red carpet. The trees and bushes above it were like red ghosts, bending under heavy clusters of insects. Here and there in the frightening landscape were human figures, as unrecognizable as beings from another planet. Either they had come to a dead halt or they moved with a great effort, as if glued to the ground.

The scenes described are taken from, or rather inspired by, the migratory locusts' invasion of Morocco in November, 1954, which seems to me to be a typical and important example of these insects' movements and their destructive powers. Within ten minutes the orange trees of the Sous valley were stripped down to the bark, and all the ground vegetation was eaten away. Here alone the damage was estimated at three billion francs. It was hoped to bring certain plantations back to normal within two years; others would require five to ten.

Data for a full reconstruction of the development of this

disaster are still lacking; and some episodes in my dramatic narrative are not located exactly as they took place. The helicopter, I believe, has not been used against insect clouds in Morocco; but it has been used elsewhere—in Madagascar, for example—and it has been brought into this story so that no important device used against the Eighth Plague may be omitted. In brief, taking details all of which are matters of fact, I have worked them into a mosaic faithful to the general course of events in 1954, but elaborated to give a complete picture of a scourge which repeatedly, over the centuries, has brought devastation in its train. Since the present book is concerned with animal migration, there are a few more words to be said about the end of the 1954 invasion.

The locusts, gorged with food, were attacked in the very place where they had committed their worst depredation. Incalculable numbers of them perished, leaving an appalling stench behind them. A few—very few—survivors did fly away. Their pursuers looked indifferently at the scattered squadrons which whirled for a few moments above the crimson slaughterhouse, then flew off to the north.

Some of the survivors were too deeply poisoned by the acricide to remain more than a few hours in the air, and they fell, leaving fewer and fewer companions to continue on their way. And what was their final destination? Inevitably, the sea, which encloses the large land area of Africa, as well as that of all other continents, on every side. But the sea is not necessarily an obstacle in the locusts' way. In 1945 and 1947 some of the *Locusta migratoria* species traveled, through generations, from the flooded zone of the Niger as far as southwestern France. Schistocerca itself often crosses the Red Sea on the way from Arabia to Africa; but it has never been known to go from North Africa to Western Europe.

The essential mechanism of locust migration is still incompletely known. It seems—although extreme caution is in order—that for many species the journey ends in definite dispersal. The locusts from the zones favorable to the development of the gregarious and migratory character perish, leaving no descendants. This may or may not be the general rule; but *Schistocerca gregaria*, the locust of the Bible, does not follow it.

The locusts which escaped the great massacre of 1954 changed color before reaching the sea. They put on their yellow marriage dress and, like their parents, accomplished the act of procreation. Thousands of larvae were deposited in the earth, and these developed into winged insects with the same migratory impulse. But the impulse drove them not toward the north—that is, into the sea—but toward the south. The whole species made an about-turn. Small waves, in no way comparable to the great destructive clouds, made the opposite trip, from North Africa to Mauritania. Here is to be played the next act, whose conclusion is still unpredictable.

On these largely desert expanses the generations descended from the survivors of the great invasion reproduce their kind. If various circumstances—temperature, atmospheric pressure, humidity—are propitious, the larvae will be born in such numbers that the species will become gregarious and soon after wing its way to the north. Otherwise *Schistocerca gregaria* will again become *Schistocerca flaviventris*. The gray-green locusts will remain isolated, hiding timidly in the bushes. For years no assembly of militarized larvae will take place on the ground. For the migratory cycle to start again, thousands of miles away on the deserts of Arabia a wave of humid air will have to multiply the larvae and rekindle the ardor of what we know from the book of Exodus as the Eighth Plague.

CHAPTER V

THE RACE TO DESTRUCTION

I am a lemming. For generations we lemmings lived happily on our plateau. Our life was divided into day and night. By day we were cautious and lay low, never venturing far from our burrows. At dusk we ran in all directions about our domain, but without ever crossing its natural boundaries. We ate grass and young plants and nibbled at the tender bark of the birches. When night came, if it was not too cold, we stayed outside several hours longer, to look for food or else to gambol beneath the stars. Week after week went by, and the daytime lengthened until it was always daylight. It was then that we approached the females. Under the impulsion of desire every lemming looked for a female that pleased him, and he began by rubbing his nose against hers. Usually there was no rivalry or violence of any kind. Every couple had once a year, sometimes twice, a litter of five or six little lemmings. Then once more life was divided into day and night; the night lengthened until it was always night, and the ground was covered with snow. We slept in burrows lined with grass, with a layer of frozen sod to protect us from the cold above, waking from time to time to eat from our store of food. Occasionally we went through an underground gallery to a hole through which we could peer outside. Outside was nothing but darkness, cold, and snow. Quickly we scuttled back into the burrow. Later day would return, and the cycle would begin all over again. In those times we were happy.

Then why did everything have to change? Why did misfortune descend upon our peaceful race instead of upon wolves and other animals of prey? Here, on the strange shore where I have come, a few dozen lemmings, remnants of our mighty race, lie numb and exhausted; those that are not dead are doubtless dying, and perhaps I may soon be among them. How am I to explain? I am myself a victim of the pitiless fatality which drove us thus far and will drive me still farther if by some miracle my strength returns. And yet I must tell what I understand of our story.

Will the reader forgive me for putting words into the mouth of a lemming? "A rat! A rat!" Hamlet would doubtless have cried, had he seen one. Halfway between a rat and a guinea pig, a miniature marmot that nimbly glides rather than steps over the ground—and oh, what silky fur, tawny with brown spots, and a lighter shade on the paws and belly! And a keen, almost intelligent look in the eye. May I credit the brain lodged in this slender, pointed head with sufficient acumen for the owner to tell his own story? Why not, if this is the most convincing way to tell it? The scorn of scientists for the pathetic fallacy of anthropomorphism holds no terrors for me. The lemmings' incredible adventure does not stem from an abstract idea, beyond their intellectual powers, but from a sentimental disturbance, provoked by a glandular modification. Once we have cleared away the legends of days gone by—the first observers of the lemmings believed that they had fallen, like rain, from the sky!—it seems that their migratory impulse, like that of the other creatures which we have studied, is the result of a shift in the neuroendocrine balance. Here again we come across the key which we have already found several times. After all, we humans change our behavior in the same way, because of an impulse which originates in our glands. Like our animal brothers, we are mysteriously inclined to fall in love, write poetry, or embark on some other adventure which beclouds our logic and makes us heedless of perils which our reasoning power should point out along the way.

This is one reason why, without doing anything so ridiculous as to compare a lemming's intelligence to that of a man, I have dared to press him into service as a narrator. A story told in the first person seems to me to be more direct and dramatic. And my last scruples are swept away when I recall that Professor Budker, the eminent cetologist, made a humpback whale the hero of a short story.

The lemmings of Norway (Myodes lemmus) *live in the northernmost part of the country, on high plateaus. Now I shall turn the story over to my narrator. Occasionally—but as infrequently as possible—I shall interrupt him, in order to supply some facet of the picture which he could not have observed.*

It all began because there were so many of us. But it was some time before I took that in. I have no idea of the population of our colony when I was very young. We met in the galleries of our burrows and also outside, but we never all went out at the same time; and every family clung to a nest of its own. As soon as a lemming grows up, he establishes himself independently. We were sociable, to be sure, but nothing more. We rubbed noses when we met and tussled amicably with one another, especially when we were young, but that was all. Generally, it was each one for himself, and the devil take the hindmost. We had no desire to live in large

numbers in the same nest within the burrow, and, when I
went out, I preferred to go by myself. The twilight season,
when the sun did not blind my eyes, suited me best. On certain days a damp mist gave our surroundings a cottony look,
in which no shape stood out distinctly. Birds, which I could
hear but not see, flew overhead, no other lemming was in
sight, and I felt as if I were quite alone. I nibbled blades of
dewy grass and dug into the earth for roots; I leaped over
the rocks with my heart pounding in my breast. As soon as
I felt the least bit tired I came back to one of the entrances
of our burrow, scurrying along the trail left by my own
smell. I knew that I might fall asleep suddenly, within a
matter of seconds; and, no matter how pleasurable a sensation this might be, it was fraught with danger. Cold and
many other enemies lie in wait for a lemming that falls
asleep outside his home.

I kept my taste for these solitary walks even after I had
founded a family. My mate took care of the young, occasionally making excursions of her own. Once the young were
grown, I left her and returned to my own little nest. Such
was our monotonously peaceful, happy life, the life of millions of little people who never cause talk.

One day toward the end of winter, I left my nest in the
burrow for one of the exits from our underground city. Certain galleries opened up near bushes or trees whose bark
was particularly tasty, and I had a sudden longing for fresh
food. Along the way I was overtaken by three lemmings who,
instead of following me quietly, pushed ahead. One of them
even emitted an irritated cry. These manners surprised me.
When I reached the exit, I looked prudently around to see
what was going on outside.

The snowy ground glistened in the light of the moon,

punctuated by dark masses of rock. A few steps away some lemmings were nibbling at the bark of dwarf birches. I hadn't expected to see so many. Crawling clumps of them swarmed over the snow-covered bushes, transforming them into little islands of black amid the general whiteness. They did not eat in the usual restrained way, but wriggled and pushed one another around, as they streamed first toward the trees and then away, bumping and crying aloud. Farther off, other lemmings were leaping in the snow, and beyond them in every direction were others still. What utter madness! I shouldn't have been surprised to hear that some rash creatures, overcome by cold and fatigue, were lying frozen and dead. What a killing a silent, predatory owl could have made, had it swooped down upon this unruly conglomeration!

Two other lemmings came, or rather burst, out of the burrow beside me. They shot forward, whirled around a group nibbling at one of the bushes, and then ran on until they were gone from sight. While I was staring at this most unusual spectacle, my heart began to beat faster. I stood hesitantly at the exit, waiting for the most favorable moment to proceed, when gradually an urge to run and leap with my fellows came over me. I had lost and forgotten the hunger for fresh food which had brought me this far. At present, I wanted to move, in a way I had never imagined before, and my heart was beating faster and faster. I threw myself forward, leaping and running in circles through the snow. I rushed into a crowd of my fellows, shoving them aside, in order to have a taste of the birch bark. But a few bites were quite enough. I turned around and pressed back through the mob. I didn't even know that, like the others, I was emitting shrill cries.

How long this excitement lasted, I have not the remotest

idea. At a certain point I had a sensation of piercing cold in my nose. Apparently I hadn't altogether lost my reason, because I immediately obeyed this warning signal and plunged back into the burrow. The gallery was crowded with lemmings who, like myself, were trying to reach their nests while others pressed toward the outside. We knocked against one another in the darkness, still crying. At last I got to my nest and, dead-tired, fell into a deep sleep.

The series of events I have just described took place several times in succession. Every time it began in the same way: I woke up to hear a loud, shuffling noise in the galleries, and immediately I too felt an urge to dash about outside. When I came back I was invariably exhausted; but day by day the period of sleeping grew shorter, and I would wake abruptly, to hear shuffling and cries. Our underground city, which once upon a time had been such an oasis of peace, was now a place of tumult and disorder, to which I was increasingly unwilling to return. And I was aware that the other lemmings felt the same way. We were no longer happy, but none of us could tell why.

Winter was over. At first the sun only grazed the snow; but then it rose gradually higher above the horizon. We lemmings went out, still tumultuously, into the long twilight and ate greedily of the vegetation bared by the melting snow. We ventured far from the burrow, and many of us fell victim to the silent swoop of an owl or to a buzzard dropping like a stone out of the sky. Almost every day an ermine came out of the rocks. Before we had any inkling of its presence it was among us, a flash of white zigzagging over the ground; and as we fled in terror we heard the victims' cries. But nothing seemed to teach us a lesson. The next day we ventured forth just as rashly as before, and were just as reluctant to go home.

About this time I began to understand why we were less and less contented with our underground city: the place was overpopulated. We still had our individual and family nests; but they were too close together, and the galleries were always crowded. We dug into the earth in order to widen them, and this caused parts of the roof and walls to crumble. We seemed to be destroying our own burrow, and it became all the more detestable, so that now we actively wanted to go away. But where? When we went outside there were so many of us that we felt uncomfortable and ill at ease. I wanted to escape, not only from the noisy, overcrowded burrow, but also from the mass of lemmings all over our domain, to recover somehow the peace and quiet I had known in other days. This very nostalgia served to disquiet me, and I could see that the same was true of my fellows. All of us were in constant irritation, and every meeting served as the pretext for a quarrel. Instead of rubbing noses in friendly fashion, we uttered shrill cries, spat in one another's faces and fought ferociously.

As the days lengthened, the mating season came around. But that which had been so pleasurable in other years was now sheer hell. Desire was overpowering, and our new pugnaciousness caused us to fight over possession of the females, in spite of the fact that there were plenty of them. At the least affront lemmings fought to the death. We do not eat flesh of any kind, and the dead bodies rotted and raised a stench on the ground.

Into this horrid atmosphere the new generation was born. Amazingly enough, the little ones grew faster than their parents and grandparents; they soon became just as active, excitable, and hostile as ourselves. We realized into what fantastic disorder our race had fallen when we saw young males, at an age when we had been hardly more than children, seeking out the females and fighting furiously for them. And the worst of it was that we ourselves suddenly had the same desire and found ourselves battling with our own progeny just as we had recently battled among ourselves. Females who up to that time had produced one or two litters a year now brought forth three or even four, and their daughters gave birth beside them.

It was obvious that this state of things could not endure. Our city was uninhabitable; we had all reached a climax of exasperation and felt an overpowering urge to go, to go anywhere at all as long as it was far enough away. Our departure took place one morning, when swarming crowds of lemmings were clustered about every exit from the burrow. At a certain moment this promiscuity was so unpleasant that I clambered up onto the branch of a tree, whence I had a view of all our people. The sight was distressing and comic at the same time. Lemmings ran and leaped in every direction, crying aloud and biting one another. Suddenly a single male emerged from the crowd immediately below me. He ran in the direction opposite to that of the sun and started down over the edge of the cliff. None of us had ever left the plateau. But this fellow dared to cross our natural boundary and to keep right on going, apparently with no intention of turning back.

His example produced an instantaneous and dynamic effect. Four, ten, thirty lemmings ran after him, over the cliff and then straight ahead, as if some madness were propelling them. I looked hard, and my heart pounded. A second later, *I* jumped down from the tree and followed. When I reached the edge of the plateau I turned around and saw a great column of lemmings speeding toward me. Some remained near the openings of the burrow, and a few had even gone back inside; but the immense majority was scurrying toward me. We all went over the cliff, in a solid brown torrent, together.

Every colony of lemmings had pullulated in the same way, although the year seemed to be in all respects an average year. Some scientists remarked that the preceding summer had been unusually warm, but others refused to connect this fact with the lemmings' unusual proliferation—a phenomenon which had taken place many times before under different circumstances. Regardless of heat or cold, there was every now and then a "lemming year," for no comprehensible reason. The cycle was irregular, coming around at intervals of four, five, ten or even more years.

The lemmings themselves understood least of all why they had multiplied so intensely this particular year. They became not only prolific, but anxious and unstable as well. Irritated by their own abundance, they left their homes and their homeland. They would have been terrified if, during the period of their own fertility, they could have seen what was going on in the nests of the Arctic owls, buzzards and other birds of prey, to whose beaks and claws Nature has entrusted maintenance of the equilibrium in lemming population. For the young of all these birds were coming into the world in increasing numbers as well. Female rough-legged buzzards had laid five or six eggs instead of the usual three or four; great white owls, eight or ten instead of five or six; and so on, all along the line. Their death squadrons were ready to take to the air with greater striking power than usual.

It was not easy to ascertain whether the lemmings' land

enemies—ermines, foxes, and other carnivorous animals—
had multiplied in the same proportions, for all of them were
expert at concealing their lairs. During this particular season, the local inhabitants saw an unusually large number of
them, and all those they saw were moving away from the
plateaus and in the same westward direction. They wound
down the sides of the valleys, walking or trotting toward the
lowlands where sooner or later the torrents of lemmings were
bound to pass. It seemed as if some invisible strategist were
marshaling his air and land forces to exterminate the surplus
lemming population.

In this same region another event, not directly connected
with the lemmings, took place in the "lemming year." Animals that had had no association with them, small rodents
and non-predatory birds, also multiplied to an unusually
large degree. A phenomenon in some remote part of the
universe must have been to blame. A mysterious radiation
had struck a restricted area of our planet and caused an increase of animal vitality. There was no apparent change in
either climate or vegetation, but several species of animals
and birds had multiplied beyond measure. And the lemmings'
hereditary enemies had grouped their air and land armies
and started to march against them.

The slope which we descended upon our departure led to
a valley wide enough for our column to spread out. This
thinning of our ranks afforded us a certain physical relief.
We proceeded at a good clip over the damp ground, but our
movements were no longer frenzied. Some twenty lemmings
followed directly on the heels of the leader, and the rest of
us came after.

We kept on walking all that day and through the night,

with the murmur of a river at our right side. In the morning we stopped to sleep, without digging burrows because we expected, as soon as we had rested sufficiently, to set off again. The spring grass was richer and tastier than that which grew on our plateau. We proceeded in this fashion several days, or rather nights, because we always walked in the dark and stopped at dawn.

One night we found a river ahead. The valley made an abrupt turn toward the south, and our destination was the west. Our law was to follow the sun, and had been from the moment we had left our city. Without knowing why, we should have died rather than transgress it. Now our leader advanced unhesitatingly into the water, followed by his immediate group and then all the rest of us. I had always liked dampness, but had never ventured into the water. In spring and autumn, when ponds formed on our plateau, I always went around them. But now, just as promptly as the others, I plunged in and quite naturally began to swim. The river did not flow too rapidly, and my light coat of fur actually seemed to hold me up. With my head and shoulders out of the water, I paddled along, among the floating mass of lemmings. Before I knew it, I was on the opposite shore.

This first swim gave me a most agreeable impression. The plunge into cold water had relaxed my nerves marvelously. My companions must have had the same feeling because, after we had shaken ourselves dry, we lingered on the river bank, peacefully eating the green grass, without jostling one another. Here and there lemmings even rubbed noses together in a friendly way. It seemed as if, by some miracle, we had rediscovered the urbanity of the happy life we had lived in the old days. Were we going to stop and settle down in this

richly productive valley? No, indeed. Our nerves were relaxed, but we still felt a sovereign urge to keep going.

The next night, continuing westward up the slope, we
came upon a wide, rolling, wooded plateau. Over this we
walked a long time—a number of weeks, if I remember correctly. We had to cross several valleys running at right angles
to our predetermined course, but every time we found ourselves again on the plateau; and there we experienced the
last peaceful part of our journey. Spread out on a wide front,
we progressed slowly, frequently stopping for several days
at a time. We were not hurried travelers, but a great people,
accomplishing a dignified exodus. Males and females knew
one another, and a new generation was born. We moved at so
leisurely a rate that the families thus formed had time to
overtake those of us that had gone ahead.

In all the time that we had been marching, including this
last period on the plateau, not one of our enemies had, to my
knowledge, been seen. Perhaps some of my companions, out
of my range, were attacked and killed; but I knew nothing
about it. We were traveling by brief stages, under cover of
darkness (the nights were becoming shorter and shorter), and
the wooded terrain afforded us protection. By day we took
shelter under the low, overhanging branches of trees.

My first realization that circumstances were changing came
when other lemmings came closer around me. The plateau
was narrowing. Soon it ended, and we went down into a
high-walled valley, with a swift stream at our left. Once more
we had to proceed in close formation, and this crowding
irritated us. It seemed hardly worth while to have left our
early home and traveled so far only to fall back into the same
promiscuity. You may say that the individualists among us
(alas, I was one!) had only to turn around and go back to the

hospitable, rolling plateau, or else climb up one side of the valley and find another line of travel; but both these alternatives were equally impossible. No thought of retracing our steps ever crossed our minds, and an invincible force compelled us to follow our leader toward the setting sun. This fatality, which forced us into close quarters every time that there was a narrowing of our path, made us unhappy. We were carrying with us the very unhappiness which we had hoped to leave behind. And yet this unhappiness was only a trifle compared to what was shortly to descend upon us.

The birds' first attack took place one early morning, when we had just arrived at a turn in the valley and begun climbing the slope in order to continue westward. Hearing some lemmings cry out at my right, I looked and saw two pairs of great wings flapping near the ground and lemmings bounding away in all directions. Already right and left, before and behind me, more buzzards were dropping like stones out of the sky. Only a few steps away a bird—it seemed to me to be perfectly enormous—was beating his wings over the body of a lemming it had nailed to the ground, while its powerful beak smashed the cranium and forced out the oozing brain. Cries of terror rose from all sides, and we ran blindly against one another, our hearts pounding.

Suddenly my nose was glued to a vertical wall of earth by a solid mass of lemmings pressing against my back. I scratched the earth with all my might. Behind me the buzzards cried out in triumph, and the lemmings in pain. Several of us were squeezed against the wall, clawing at it in a vain attempt to dig in and find protection. Tunneling into the earth is child's play to us, and we do it at incredible speed. But now we were all pushed together and suffocating for lack of air. The cries of panic behind me continued for what seemed an endless time. All the buzzards of the region must have gathered for the attack. How many victims would it take to satisfy their hunger? With my companions pressing at my back, I clawed on, in a state of utter exhaustion. Probably I should have died of fatigue or asphyxia had not the pressure gradually diminished, letting me pause for breath. Turning halfway around, I saw the light outside the hole which we had succeeded in digging. There were no more cries; obviously the buzzards' attack was over. I was so tired that I sank into sleep on the spot, among my companions.

I was awakened by renewed cries and once more felt myself pressed against the ground. It was still light outside our hole, and another attack had descended from the air. Along with the lemmings to either side of me, I dug frantically deeper into the cliff.

I have no idea how many times the buzzards attacked us on the side of the valley. At first we dug in only when the pressure of our companions sounded the alarm; but eventually we took advantage of every moment when our strength was restored to extend our shelter, shifting the direction of our tunnel until it ran in the direction of the setting sun. Even underground this direction was now part of our consciousness. More than once we had to tunnel around obstacles, and every time we ended by digging toward the west. The humidity of the earth and the roots of plants let us know how far we were from the surface. After a while we began to dig obliquely upward. The roots grew more thickly, and the earth was increasingly damp. A little more effort, and we emerged. It was the dead of night, and the stars were shining in the sky. We were too exhausted to think of food, and fell at once into deep sleep.

This side of the valley was an accursed place. Day and

night we were attacked by the birds—the silent great white owls swooped down as we nibbled the plants—and the foxes. The strong odor of the foxes put us on our guard, and we leaped toward the tunnels; but never quickly enough to prevent a few of our number from falling into their grasp. The foxes that made a catch withdrew, but others took their place. Our cliffside refuge was like a besieged fortress, as the foxes tore at it with their big claws.

To stay here meant death. And this too must be said: even without this danger we should have gone away. The promiscuity of the tunnel was just as intolerable as the overcrowding of our native city, and the urge to go west was as invincible as ever. When, one evening, a new leader gave the signal for departure, we followed him like one man. The departure from the besieged city was marked by a terrible slaughter. Foxes rose up from the earth, and birds of prey swooped down from the sky. So much the worse! At this point nothing could stop us, and we were not in the least afraid to die. We were so highly charged that we were beside ourselves. In the course of this slaughter most of us, when a fox arrived, turned to face him, spat in his face, and even bit his lips. There could be only one issue to such an encounter; but the sight of our murdered fellows did not stop us or turn us away from the route we were predestined to follow.

The frame house was a bright red spot among the dark green firs which bordered the pale blue water. At one side were the stable and two barns; beyond them, an empty pasture with a fence running around it. At this distance from the sea the fjord looked like a river, overcast by the shadow of the dark green opposite shore. The season of interminable days was over; the hay, barley, and rye all had been stored in the barns. On the flat ground in the distance were some primitive huts, and goats grazing.

Old Catherine was sitting in the kitchen. She was sitting in an armchair, with her gnarled hands on the handle of her cane, staring straight ahead. Her eyes were quite good enough to see the opposite wall and all the objects around her, but she was not looking. All her attention was concentrated in her ears. Ever since the others had gone away, leaving her alone, she had sat there, listening. "We'll be back before the night is over. Everything will be all right; don't worry. Better not light the fire. Go to bed early; that way you'll be sure of keeping warm." The village where they were holding the yearly celebration was not far away. And the young people were quite right to have gone, taking the children with them, even the baby that was not yet weaned. Young people are entitled to their fun. Day after day of hard work, and soon— my God, how soon!—they too will find themselves grown old, sitting quite uselessly in an armchair, almost as good as dead. And then, what is left? Only memories.

"Yes, of course," Catherine had told them. "Don't worry about me. I shall go early to bed."

But she had not gone to bed; she remained motionless in her chair. In her mind she pictured one after another, sharply and exactly, every room in the house, then the barns, the chicken coop, the stable. In the stable the old mare, too, was alone; the two younger horses were harnessed to the carts in which the rest of the family had gone away. A single animal in the stable; no trouble could come there. The cows had been watered and fed and now were quietly ruminating in one of the barns. Not a sound from that direction, or from the chicken coop, where the hens would soon tuck their heads under their wings and sleep. Catherine's thoughts returned to the various rooms of the house. They were all empty, and the furniture could not stir. Nothing was going to happen. No fire was lit, either in the house or anywhere near, and there was no possible danger.

Suddenly a dog barked, and the old woman started. Yes, there were the dogs, too, but they were no cause for fear. Barns, stable, and chicken coop all were tightly closed and in good order. Then a second dog barked along with the first. A visitor? Who could it possibly be, on this of all nights? And there was no sound of a horse and cart approaching. Still the dogs continued to bark. The best thing was to go have a look outside. With a slight effort, Catherine rose to her feet. Once she was standing up, she did not have too much trouble walking. She peered out the window, but there was nothing on the road as far as she could see. The dogs were on the opposite side, and she went to another window and threw it open just in time to see three dogs running away, still barking. A moment later they were out of sight, around a corner of the house.

Leaning on her cane, Catherine walked to the door and out into the courtyard. Once she was a few steps from the house, she had a broad view, as far as the huts. The goats were leaping about from one side to the other, and the dogs were barking as if they had caught the scent of a hare. But no hare has ever scared a goat. Could it be a wolf? At this season, it seemed unlikely. And the dogs would never have gone barking after a wolf. Their only thought would be to avoid him.

Catherine held one hand over her eyes and peered into the distance; but she could not see clearly. The goats seemed to have disappeared, and the only sound in the deserted countryside was the intermittent barking of the dogs. They seemed to be coming nearer and nearer. A moment later, at the edge of the pasture, the dogs came into sight. They were zigzagging over the ground, jumping, barking and stopping every now and then to bite. At the same time a big cat came dashing toward the courtyard, with something in her mouth. What was it, a rat, a bird? The cat ran behind the house. Meanwhile just beyond the bare earth of the courtyard, the grass at the edge of the pasture began to wave. Then a line of moving brown things glided out onto the bare ground, and Catherine knew them at once for lemmings.

Four or five times, at least, in her long life, she had seen them, and she knew that the farm straddled their path; in other years they had devoured many a farmer's grain. Now her first thought was: "Thank God, this time they've come too late. The harvest is in." But the lemmings were all over the courtyard, and as she saw them around her feet she remembered: "I never shut the door!"

The lemmings were advancing on a wide front, which opened and spread out around the farm buildings, like the waters of a stream. In the stable the mare was whinnying. Catherine walked as fast as she could, with the lemmings around her. They poured by the door without entering, pushing one another and emitting shrill cries. At the edge of the pasture the dogs were still barking. Looking through the open door, Catherine saw that the lemmings had invaded the kitchen, or rather that a solid stream of them was crossing it. They came not through the door but through the open window, on the left side, and they were flowing out of the opposite window, having broken two panes of glass. They jumped up over the chairs and table without pausing and without deviating an inch from their predestined direction.

Catherine stepped into the kitchen, raising her cane. She went toward the open window, striking out at the lemmings along the way. Every now and then one sank his sharp teeth into her foot or tugged at her apron, so that she had to hold onto the table in order not to fall. The lemmings reacted against her attack by crying and spitting; those that were scurrying across the table made as if to jump at her face. Catherine drew back, trembling. She knew that the lemmings were not dangerous to man, or indeed to any animal. But her feeling of impotence was profoundly disturbing. She had left the window open, and now there was nothing she could do. What would the young people say when they came home? Dear God, what would they say?

The dogs' barking came from the courtyard now. Four dogs and two cats, their jaws dripping with blood, were butchering as many lemmings as they could handle. Every one on which they laid a paw tried to defend himself before their teeth closed upon him, while his fellows streamed by, shrilly crying. The cows had joined their mooing to the mare's whinny. They too were aware that something terrifying was going by.

Leaning against the doorpost, Catherine closed her eyes and wept. She was a weak, miserable creature, and now she was trembling from the cold. How long must this nightmare go on? Possibly for many hours to come. The daylight was fading, and soon it would be night.

Catherine opened her eyes. From the stable there came a frightful crash as loud as cannon fire. Somehow, the lemmings must have forced their way in. How could it have happened? But that was it, for sure. The excited mare was kicking with all her might at the slats which separated her stall from the rest of the stable. Catherine's heart beat faster as the meaning was borne in on her. This was almost the

*worst thing that could have happened. The mare might hurt
herself or even die. She must be saved before it was too late.*

*Catherine made her way across the courtyard, among the
swarming lemmings. The lemmings cried, the dogs barked,
the cows mooed; and above this depressing medley rose the
cannon shots from the stable. Catherine walked courageously
toward the cannon. As she drew near the stable door, she
saw that the lemmings had dug a passage underneath it. A
stream of them must be flowing between the mare's legs and
sending her into a panic. Catherine transferred her cane to
her left hand and turned the heavy key. There. All she had to
do now was pull the wooden bar over to the right.*

*Only the left-hand section of the stable door could be
opened; the other was barred on the inside.*

*The sound of the mare's swinging hoofs drowned out all
the rest of the noise; Catherine felt as if she were hemmed in
by thunder. Harassed by the lemmings which bit at her feet
as they went by, she tugged, all too slowly, at the heavy bar.
The mare must have heard her approach, for now she was
kicking at the wall side of her stall. Unfortunately, this meant
that she was pushing against the door; and the old woman's
tugging was in vain. Breathlessly she came back to the middle. The bar had all but slipped free of the last ring, but the
pressure of the mare's body was holding it. It can't hold long,
thought Catherine, for the bar was acting as a lever, and the
end was starting to crack under the strain. Catherine drew
back; but the sound of the mare's furious kicking prevented
her from thinking clearly, and she did not move out of the
way. A second later the bar broke; there was a hole in the
door, and in a flash she saw the mare thrust out her wounded
head, with madness in her eyes. Something hit her and
knocked her down. Then nothing more.*

Night had fallen. A stream of lemmings was still flowing across the kitchen of the empty house, which by now was filled with cold air. Outside, other branches of the same stream poured around the farm buildings, and the lemmings cried out at intervals as in their excitement they bit one another. The dogs had eaten their fill and fallen into an exhausted silence. In front of the swinging stable door lay old Catherine's inanimate body. The lemmings passed to right and left, leaving it untouched and unsullied.

The season of interminable days had gone by. Every day the sun descended several hours below the horizon, plunging the earth into darkness. Just as at the beginning of our exodus, we could have traveled under this protection and stopped to rest by day. But we had thrown prudence to the winds, and indeed, at this point, we hardly knew what we were doing.

We pushed on, sometimes by night, sometimes a night and day together, sleeping in sheer exhaustion the next night and setting out again at dawn, when we were exposed and vulnerable. Repeated attacks had reduced our numbers perhaps by half. Foxes trailed us almost unceasingly through the valleys, dropping back only when they had had their fill and then catching up with us again when they were hungry. Our only real respite occurred when the wolves, who were following at a greater distance, fell upon the foxes they found in their way. At such times the foxes made themselves scarce. If they failed to return, then the wolves attacked us directly. From the sky we were attacked not only by our old enemies but also by unknown birds which had flown out of the west to meet us. We were a most desirable prey, and an object of dispute to a host of aggressors.

Still we pushed on. We did not stop to eat, but nibbled at whatever we found in our direct path. There was a fixed, obsessive stare in our glassy eyes, and we were almost always filthy. In spite of the invincible force that impelled us, our coats were bedraggled and dull, and we had a sickly air. Only when we had just come out of the water did we have a more or less normal aspect. We crossed numerous rivers and lakes, and every time that we shook ourselves dry on the far shore we felt momentarily less unhappy and somewhat relaxed. But this comfortable feeling did not last long; in fact, every time it grew shorter. Almost immediately we became again harried, jostling migrants, heedless of the massacres that the morrow was sure to bring.

Perhaps if we had lingered several days beside some river or lake and bathed in it over and over we might have been delivered from our frenzy. But we had to go on. We did not think to seek out soothing water, but merely swam across any body of it that we found in our path and then implacably continued in the same direction. Always the same direction.

We moved blindly; and yet when I look back at these days and try to relive them I can better define this impulse, which was, to all outward appearances, completely mad. I remember now that I had a vague feeling that we must press on, come what might, because beyond all our difficulties there was *something* which, once reached, would be our salvation, which would restore us to our old selves and the happy tranquillity of former times. We were marching, in defiance of danger and death, toward a Promised Land, toward a liberation which was surely awaiting us at the end of our journey. We knew not when or how we should find it, but we were sure that it was there; and this certainty impelled us, every one.

Several times we came to places inhabited by men. At the beginning of our journey the sight of these vertical creatures might have intimidated us; but at this point we had such a sovereign desire to go forward that men were no more terrifying to us than other enemies. Moreover, they were far less numerous. One day, upon our arrival in a human city, we found a stone obstacle extending a considerable distance to either side of our path. We dug tunnels, and the one in which I was engaged had to be extended a long way, because every time we came near the surface we smelled dogs and heard their scratching and barking mingled with the voices of men. We ran into underground walls, which made it necessary to dig even deeper, and stones fell, obstructing our tunnel. Dramatic and horrible struggles took place in the dark. When, along with a few of my fellows, I finally returned above ground, the dogs were waiting. I heard bones cracking between their teeth, but once more managed to flee, continuing always in the same direction.

Not once, but many times more. I have no idea how many of those who had journeyed all the way from our original home were still alive when we reached the boundless water. For some time we had been following a river, and now, at its mouth, our column advanced over a wide, sandy expanse sloping into the sea. The water had a smell different from that of any we had seen so far. In spite of all the births that had taken place among us, we were far less numerous than at our departure, and all of us together covered no more than a small part of the beach, in scattered formation. Still, to our left, and also to our right, beyond the river's mouth, the sand was dotted by thousands of lemmings. Rivers of lemmings poured down toward the sea, fanning out as they descended. This was the end of the road for the other groups of lemmings, as well as our own; the survivors of all the exoduses came together and along the beach, from north to south, leaped toward the water.

There was not a single man or fox on the sand. Our terrestrial enemies had abandoned the chase. But birds of prey from the sea were flying low over the waves. At some distance from the shore, but well this side of the horizon, were some small islands, indistinct in the mist. Between the shore and the islands the waves were dotted with an infinity of tiny brown spots, the heads of swimming lemmings.

A violent, icy wind penetrated our fur, and the full fatigue of our long march was upon us. But in spite of weariness and cold, we were more feverish than ever, and the salty smell of the sea acted like a magnet. We realized that we must plunge, without delay, into this great mass of water. It alone could calm our fever and set us free. Without ever having seen it, we had marched toward the sea, and now we bounded forward, indifferent to the gulls and cormorants that swooped down ceaselessly, uttering harsh cries. It was intoxicating to feel the damp sand beneath our feet as we crossed it to plunge into the surf.

I found myself floating more easily in the sea than in the fresh water of rivers and lakes. Although the waves tossed me about, I rose and fell with them. In front of me and on either side, an infinite number of tiny heads and shoulders were similarly rising and falling. The sea cradled us, and we moved our paws vigorously in order to swim. Great crying birds descended upon our fleet, flapping their wings on a level with the water, then slowly rising, with victims in their beaks. At times a dark shadow came up from below, a pointed mouth broke the surface of the water, and another lemming disappeared from view. Such sights made no impression upon me. I continued to swim, drunk with happiness, feeling as free as any one of these swift fish.

But I found out that I was not a fish when I began to feel less comfortable in the water. My fur, which had been light and airy, now stuck to my body and weighed me down. My shoulders were lower in the water, and only my head emerged. Far ahead I could make out the hazy outline of the islands. I was still swimming, but it seemed as if the lemmings around me were less numerous. I passed many that were virtually drifting. Their heads hung down in the water, and only the wet fur on their backs was visible. The farther I swam, the more of them I saw in this condition. They were no longer advancing, but bobbed up and down in obedience to the motion of the waves. Birds picked them off, or fish snapped at them from below.

I was tired and cold. There seemed to be no end to the sea. Sometimes the foamy crest of a wave went over my head. Around me, some lemmings floated inertly while others began to sink, and I could see them descending through the green water. Farther away, others still were swimming, like myself, toward the nearest island. I had been overcome by desire at first sight of the sea and had thrown myself drunkenly into it; now I wanted nothing but land. I wanted to feel solid ground under my feet, to stop this swimming motion, to rest and sleep. My struggle against weariness and sleep, the struggle to keep my poor little restless self alive in the middle of the sea, was of long duration. The water around me was empty except for a few drowned companions.

The sun was close to the horizon, directly ahead of me. Every time a wave slightly higher than the average lifted me up, I could see the somber profile of the island, outlined against the yellow sky. Every time, the island seemed larger

than before; but I felt as if I should never get there. I was
dead tired, and several times I must have fallen asleep for
a second, letting my head drop into the water; but the sensation of choking aroused me, and once more I moved my
paws.

I was half asleep when the island loomed up directly
before me. It was nearly night, and its opaque mass filled
my entire vision. The smell of land gave me strength, and I
swam desperately on. Now land was close, and I felt the
sand beneath me. I dragged myself up onto the beach, hardly
able to carry the weight of my body. The dark sand was
spotted with black objects which I recognized by their
smell as lemmings. Several dozen survivors of the crossing
lay there, a few yards from the sea. I went up to one and
sniffed him to make sure he was alive. He was asleep, and
soon I too fell into a drugged unconsciousness.

Suddenly I am asleep no longer. A terrible sound has
awakened me: the cry of birds. The sun is not yet up, but
beyond the sea the sky is rosy. The deafening bird calls come
from rocks directly above us. My whole body trembles, and
so does that of the lemming against which I have slept. Our
fur sticks to our skin, and we are shivering with cold. The
sun is about to rise, and the rapacious birds, ready to take
flight, are crying.

*Pitiful remnants of the exodus, what glimmer of under-
standing is left in your battered bodies? How much longer
can you endure? Will you die of cold, or in the beak of some
bird of prey, or is there a chance of your survival? Long ago,
and even in recent years, men who had seen lemmings or
heard of them used to say: "They throw themselves, of their
own accord, into the sea. Their exodus is a form of collective*

suicide." Others have hazarded: "If their migration leads to the sea, it is because they are looking for a body of land which was cast up at some former geological epoch and is now under water."

But neither of these explanations stands. I have attempted, through the mouth of a lemming, to synthesize the scientific theory of the present day. The lemmings cannot bear the tension and anxiety produced by the glandular upset which triggers their migratory impulse. They are as if overcharged. Only in liquid do they recover some balance; but even this recovery is only partial and brief. Soon the same pitiless force precipitates them into the greatest of all bodies of water, where for the last time they seek unattainable appeasement.

I have shown the lemmings marching toward the west, and it is true that those who set out in this direction follow it blindly to the end, regardless of all obstacles and dangers. Others, from other points of origin, may take a different route, but inevitably it leads to the sea. Here must be the end of their adventure. Does that adventure always end in death? The Scandinavian naturalist Hoegstroem reports that he once saw a hundred or more lemmings returning inland, to the place whence they had started. But the fact is contested. It seems probable that the rare survivors, like the narrator of our story, that reach some rocky island are doomed to perish soon after their arrival. The survival of the species is assured by a few lemmings that refuse to leave home. And how are we to explain the fact that the migratory impulse did not affect them? We are caught in a vicious circle if we answer: "Because the species must survive." We must ascertain how it happens that some few individuals escape the general disturbance; and the truth is that we do not know.

Scientists have studied the possible causes of the excessive, frenzied vitality which in certain years affects not only the lemmings but their natural enemies, and other animals of the same zone as well. Dr. P. Laurent attributes it to "a planetary, perhaps cosmic, source related to such great cyclical phenomena as volcanic eruptions, variations in global temperature, and sunspots."

This may lead us to ask whether other regions of the globe, and perhaps other species, are not similarly affected. If I were a sociologist, I should undertake a minute study of world events during the "lemming years." I might discover that dictators and statesmen, businessmen and writers, were fired, in their several areas of activity, by new will-power, or enterprise or inspiration. Of course, I might discover nothing at all. But I refuse to rule out the possibility of obtaining results from such an investigation.

The great cyclical movements of the ocean, determined by the gravitation of the spheres, affect, as we have seen, not only marine animals but mankind as well. Man is much more closely integrated with the cosmos than he generally believes. We fancy ourselves as detached spectators of the migrants' ceaseless march over the surface of our planet; but our immobility is an illusion. We too are ceaselessly changing.